Lists for Muddle Management

KayLee Parker

ISBN 1-883924-22-7
First Edition, October 2003

Company Information

List Organizer--Simple solutions for complex problems

Telephone
   435-635-2314
Postal address
   List Organizer
   P.O. Box 853
   Hurricane UT 84737
Electronic mail
   Sales and customer support: kaylee@listorganizer.com

ABOUT THE AUTHOR:

Born in California, raised in Colorado, KayLee Parker appreciates both the ocean and the mountains. Now she lives in the western desert near the red rock cliffs where the blue sky stretches on for miles. She graduated with a bachelor's degree in communications / journalism. Into her life came a husband, four children and all the pandemonium and love that come with family life. KayLee loves to read and likes to write when she feels creative so the completion of this book is another miracle in her life. Her path strayed into professional organizing in 1992 when she formed her business and began telling others how to get organized which is a natural path for a journalist and a mother. Her company, List Organizer, publishes many styles of fill-in-the-blank Lists to help people get organized. Her website, www.listorganizer.com finds millions of hits each month from people looking for an easier way to conquer the muddle in their lives.

DEDICATION

The human body produces headaches that I call professional headaches with the intensity and power that reach into the soul of the person with lighting bolt pain that takes over so the person relinquishes performing their normal activities. The person, no matter how competent and strong, goes into a darkened, quiet room and the professional headache wins for a few hours or days. Then when the person recovers and feels competent and strong again, the professional headache returns to humble that person for a second time. It's a pattern that was repeated in my life as I tried to raise four children, be a supporting wife, hold down a job and be a dedicated volunteer to numerous projects.

I believe Lewis Carroll wrote Alice in Wonderland while suffering from these professional or migraine headaches where reality slipped into another world and the mundane slipped into adventure. The concept of a Cheshire cat smiling, appearing and disappearing seemed quite normal during headache episodes. Hallucinating seems to remove the person from the pain for a while.

During these times, my husband, children and my mother, took over the house and worked around my debilitating illness. When I resurfaced from my bed, I would catch up with the schedule and chores and life went on normally until the professional headache visited again. My life was a muddle for one or two days as I struggled to get back in the routine and sometimes the muddle would remain for much longer than two days. Muddle, meaning disorder, confusion and chaos, described my life.

Struggling to keep a household functioning led me to hallucinate about the way it could be with a better organization system which was something I desperately needed. Perhaps I did develop this organization system while in a stupor of pain, or maybe, finding myself as an overwhelmed wife, mother and daughter, I searched for something better than my limited skills provided to all the family.

The family unit battled together as I tried and failed at perfecting this system. Now I look back and wish I'd had this system of Lists in place earlier in my domestic life. I believe life would have been easier for all of the family if I could have pre-planned for my moments of professional headaches, other illnesses, emergencies, frazzled schedules, emotional ups and downs, financial catastrophes and other normal life activities.

In love and appreciation for sharing those moments with me, I dedicate this book along with the Power of Lists, to my husband, Howard, my sons, Trenton and Travis, my daughters, Tanya and Torrey, and my mother, Veda Reed, all of whom supported me through the difficulties of living and my labor to help our family and others find something that would make life easier.

TABLE OF CONTENTS

(Items marked with an * are Lists, one of 125 included in the book.)

INTRODUCTION

Staying organized is a daily struggle and not something that comes naturally to me. It's taken me a lifetime to formulate this system and I've suffered many failures in my efforts to become better organized—not totally organized. The instructions and Lists in this book are as close to a magic formula for getting organized as I can develop.

List Organizer and the system of Lists function together because of my persistence in trying to find an easier way to get organized. I didn't sit down one night and decide to put together a few lists for fun. The lack of organization in my life, in the lives of my family members and in the lives of clients and friends who struggle with the grind of daily chores and schedules, made me try many systems of organization with the hope that one of them would help me.

After inventing my own organization plan and finding success in getting my life to a better standard of organization, these words came to me, "Write a book. Let your kids and others know how you manage." So I did write a book. It was a long-paged manuscript called The Organization Book Your Mother Should Have Given You. It was filled with information and a blueprint for successful living with philosophy thrown in for good measure.

"Finally," I mused. "Here is the answer to help my children and other disorganized folks." I began teaching seminars extolling the virtues of my book to others. Yet when I looked in the glazed eyes of the participants, I knew they were not going to change. My fabulous new information was not translating into new habits. After my lectures, the audience and I smiled at one another and went our separate ways--both of us wishing this information could work.

The final blow came when I gave the book to my husband and children. To my surprise, they were not interested. It was too complex. There were too many facts and these facts took too much time to learn. On and on went the excuses.

Now I was getting upset. First, no one seemed to understand the amount of work I accomplished. Now I couldn't get them to read my well prepared and researched book. Didn't they know it would help them build better personal habits? At this point I was ready to give up. People needed this information. How could I relay my knowledge to them?

My mind started creating again and came up with a new concept. I tore the book apart. I simplified the book into short lists. I trimmed the wordy fat and came up with lean information for people who want lots of information in a hurry. The basic tool used for organization is a **List**. Yet many people never make a complete, orderly usable list. So I did it for them. Pushing along with my new objective, I formed a publishing and seminar business. My business sells products your mom might have given you if she'd found the time to develop them. Now all you need is a little time and my Lists.

People tell me I have a quirky way of putting together Lists where I take large projects and slice them into little details that are easy to complete. It's the method I use to make sense of the world. It started with a grocery list I created because I couldn't find something that met my needs. Next I completed three styles of grocery lists because one style wasn't right for everybody.

Then I formulated the menu planners, the to-do lists, and next the system exploded into 125 Lists to help me get organized. I love to share this project with others who struggle with getting organized in their personal lives.

I still teach revised seminars only now the participants are happier. They are not as overwhelmed with facts and tasks and new habits. I make time management easy. Habits change. I let everyone choose how much they want to get organized. No one has to be totally organized--including my children and my husband.

My company has been featured in Lifestyle Sections in newspapers across the country. To share this information, I have appeared on television talk shows and taught classes for colleges, schools, church and business groups.

In the year 2000, I established a website named www.listorganizer.com to share some of this information. It has flourished as people throughout the world, 80 countries each month, check in to let me know that getting organized is very important to them and the Lists meet their needs. After that they share my web address with others and my business now receives millions of hits every month.

The next direction this journey has taken me is to publish a book called <u>Lists for Muddle Management</u> written for people who want information from someone who had to learn to be organized and not from a perfectionist who instinctively knew how to manage life. So I share this information with you as a woman who doesn't always "have my life together" and my house is not always spotless and some days I'm hanging on by my fingernails. Each week I follow my plan, pull out a List and know that eventually I'll find calm and peace if I can get a few more items checked off the Weekly To-Do List and the Monthly To-Do List. I've learned that things straighten out the more Lists I use and the more completed boxes that have check marks in them.

The List Organizer system has made an enormous difference in my life since it is flexible, simple, and doesn't cost much to maintain. I send this system off to the world in another book with the thought that this book will present the information in a manner so easy that no one has to fail.

One List at a time and one day at a time, I work towards keeping sanity in my schedule. It will work for you also. If you are thinking of giving up, go to the end of the book where I've pre-made a list Reasons to Give Up to save the quitters the trouble of coming up with an excuse. Instead of quitting, commit to try the system first. Good luck on your journey to better living through the Power of Lists.

Section One

List Organizer's unique system

Your Personalized Planning System

Muddle—Confusion, Chaos, Disarray, Pandemonium

Management—Control, Organize, Manage

CHAPTER ONE

Does Getting Organized take more Time than I Have?

When you moved away from home, did you wish your mother had given you an instruction book showing you how to take care of yourself? Mom hoped you had learned all there was to know by observing her example. That was a wonderful beginning, but you are not Mom, and what you want in a personal organization system is different from Mom. You need a personal planning system that is flexible, simple to use, easy to setup and to maintain.

Keep reading and you will discover that you have that organization program in your hand. Mom administered the family according to her rules. Now you can determine which of Mom's rules you want to keep in your life and which you want to change. The system taught by **List Organizer** will allow you to emphasize areas of life that you consider important and to de-emphasize the unimportant. That means you can keep your automobile maintained in tip-top shape while ignoring your messy closet. Or you can plan and prepare well-balanced meals while you give the house minimum upkeep.

Using the charts and lists in this series you will take charge of your life. You will determine which types of activities interest you and which you want to control. You get to do it your way instead of my way or Mom's way.

Enough about Mom. She did the best she could. In fact, she may have given you this book because she knows it will help you change some bad habits and develop some good habits. Compare the plan taught in this series to a diet where you get to choose your meal plans, including portions, and you still lose weight. This is your dream organization plan.

It is not a complicated system. The materials you need to start are mostly included in this book. In Chapter 5 there are instructions for buying a calendar or planner for scheduling which is an important part of time management. As you print out the Lists, you may add three ring binders or folders to store your lists. Too simple? No! Just follow the basic instructions and begin organizing your life.

Here is one of the best parts--you do not have to buy and read the entire series to begin. In fact, most of you will never try all the Lists or read all the chapters because some will not interest you. That does not matter. You may choose which parts concern you and day by day, you will establish a routine that will help you complete tasks you now struggle to perform. Since you will be dividing work into smaller segments and learning how to schedule your time, you will find keeping diverse areas of your life under control is not as hard as you thought.

When I read, I like to skim books and gather lots of good ideas in a hurry. Wordiness is not my style. Maybe it is not yours either. That is why I have tried to condense an unreasonable amount of material into charts and lists which are easy and quick to read. You benefit by receiving substantial information in a little space.

Every reader should read Chapters 1, 2, 3, and fill in the life planning charts in Chapter 3. This will assist you in discovering which parts of your life you want to organize--today, next week, and never.

The books and lists and individual packets published by List Organizer consist of charts itemizing hundreds of categorized chores which the reader can use to structure his life. Next comes the fun part. You can select which errands you like and ignore the rest. Even more important, you can decide how often you want to attend to these errands.

Next you will learn how to collect all this varied information and how to design a blueprint for daily living. The blueprint is recorded in a daily planner/personal calendar or the Weekly To-Do Lists (52 per year) or the Monthly To-Do Lists (12 per year). Each morning or night, look at your blueprint and follow through by completing the errand or, if you are too busy, reschedule it. You will be surprised how positively you will gain control of your life.

Does the work go away? Unfortunately, no. However, now you can plan ahead so it doesn't engulf you. It isn't all dull, either. You can plan the play times in life too. The difference is you won't feel guilty about taking off for fun because you have command of life's daily, weekly, and monthly responsibilities.

Begin your journey into taking care of life's little tasks. Mom would be proud.

CHAPTER TWO

Should I Keep Reading If I Hate Housework?

You are a busy person. You do not have time to worry about cleaning your house or fixing meals. You wish you could hire a personal organization expert to set-up a system tailor made to your specifications. Then you could get organized.

However, you know that experts on any subject cost more than you have and they would probably devise a system you could not implement. So you stay disorganized day after day and complain, along with all your friends, about how you never catch up and how you do not have enough time. Then you throw up your hands in disgust, resign yourself to being disorganized and take a nap while the guilt creeps into your brain. You may even tell yourself that the problem is in your genes--your mother made you disorganized.

Whatever your excuse, you cannot find the time to get organized. Your personal life is a mess and you are caught in the middle of the never ending sequence of chores, tasks, duties, responsibilities and burdens that never are completed or maybe never started.

Why didn't you learn how to take care of yourself when you were in high school? Why didn't they teach you something practical like time management? Why didn't you learn organization at home from watching Mom's example? Maybe your Mom was organized--sort of anyway. She did manage to have meals on the table, buy groceries, have shampoo in the shower, gasoline in the automobiles, and the bills paid on time. If she could do all that plus take care of you, certainly you should be able to catch on to the secrets of organization.

> Perhaps the problem isn't with you. Rather it exists because the organization system you prefer differs from the organization system anyone else would think about creating. Your priorities are not the same as your family or your friends. Mom may think making a bed is the best sign of a well-kept bedroom. Your idea of a well-kept bedroom is one where the CD's are put away and alphabetized. No wonder you are confused about what personal organization means.
>
> Or the worst may have happened--you believed that you had to be totally organized or it was not worth the effort so you gave up trying.

You may have tried to transfer your management skills from the office to the home and met with some success. At least you are able to find paper and pencils at home. You may return your personal telephone calls because you are used to recording those at the office and you transferred that skill to your home life.

Lists for Muddle Management is a buffet of choices and you get to make your choices while leaving others behind. There is no right or wrong order or answer to choosing and filling out the Lists. The Lists are your personal organization expert that is now here to help you set-up your own personal planning system. You may notice that I capitalize "the Lists" when I talk about them since they are so important to what you are going to learn and they are the foundation for personalizing your planning system.

If you are a procrastinator, you may plan your life at a slow pace so you do not become defeated. If you feel ready for a challenge, you may shift your energy into fifth gear and speed ahead. Either way is the right way to use the book and the Lists. The only judge of your progress will be yourself.

The plan is adaptable. Perhaps you start out too fast and cannot keep up. Scale back your plan and slowly add more chores. This method can easily change when you go on vacation or become ill or move. Your personal approach does not have to be scrapped just because your life changes. In fact, the true value of this plan is its flexibility.

Have I convinced you that you can take control of your life at least a little? If not, then you can convince yourself by thumbing through the Lists in the book and seeing if a few pages don't jump out at you as something you need. Then return here and keep learning about the basics of personal organization. You may find you have more time management skills than you imagined.

This is the part of the book telling you—You Can Do This. It's my small chapter to motivate you to keep going even if you have difficulties such as

1. Lazy and unmotivated
2. Have too big a family in too small a space
3. Have financial problems
4. Undisciplined
5. A chronic procrastinator
6. Too old
7. Too young
8. Suffer from ADD or depression
9. Have other health problems
10. Were told you have faulty thinking
11. Have never been organized
12. Can't remember the simplest of tasks
13. Make excuses for your life—and more excuses for everything

At the back of the book, there's a List called Reasons to Give Up where I have 37 reasons why you can't succeed at this system. It's for negative thinkers and quitters who are approaching this book with a skeptical attitude. You may want to look at that now, see how petty your excuses are and then fill in the next List which is Reasons I Can Succeed.

If you have a desire to improve your life, you can do it using Lists for Muddle Management. I've received enough letters from people over the years to know that being disorganized causes people pain and guilt. People throughout the earth have a genuine desire to gain control of their lives. They feel if they could get organized, they would have more fulfilling lives. They are correct.

So why is it so hard to organize our time and our personal lives in spite of this desire to improve? The reason you do not get organized is that you do not have the time to get organized. If it's been days since you found a pencil and a piece of paper at the same time, you will not make a "To Do List". You cannot find the time to plan your time.

The purpose of the Lists is to help you break down time management into small enough increments that you can gain control of your life. The Lists break down huge responsibilities into small tasks. You, with the instructions and lists, are going to SUBDIVIDE.

> * SUBDIVIDE tasks into smaller tasks
> * SUBDIVIDE time into smaller and more workable units
>   of time
> * SUBDIVIDE drawers, cabinets, closets, into smaller,
>   more organized areas
> * SUBDIVIDE a written record of responsibilities into
>   a calendar of manageable lists

The goal of List Organizer is to provide you, the customer, pre-made Lists containing tasks all ready subdivided. I did the work. You get the reward. The compilation of the Lists has taken ten years with many revisions and retooling of the format. This book is <u>not</u> a few lists that I threw together in my spare time. The Lists have been tested and adjusted to include important ideas. Many lists have been thrown in the trash bin since they didn't meet the needs of my clients.

The owner of this book is free to copy these Lists to use in organizing the individual and their family on a limited basis. For example, you may need to copy twelve of the Monthly To-Do list to use in one year. Most of the Lists are formatted to fit on one page for your convenience. Some of the Lists continue onto more than one page

The owner of this book may not make multiple copies of all the Lists to share with everyone they know or to teach their own time management seminar. It's a matter of limited usage and practical sense. Common sense directs that you may copy the Lists for your personal use—to help you get organized. Common sense directs that you not abuse the gift.

- The Lists are copyrighted through U.S. and International copyright laws and may not be reproduced for sale or profit.
- List Organizer publishes many of the Lists in pads or packet form for easy use. Using the published Lists, you fill-in-the-blanks and don't have to worry about copying those Lists you use again and again such as the Grocery Lists or Budget Lists. A copy of the Lists I sell may be found at <u>www.listorganizer.com/products.htm</u> or some of the products are listed on an order form at the back of this book.

CHAPTER THREE

You Can't Get There If You Don't Know Where You're Headed

Now we get to do a little planning, dreaming and goal setting. It will be great to look back at this year and say, "I've accomplished something I've always wanted to do!" If you are looking at this book, you are probably looking for answers to organization problems and that includes how to set goals and follow through on their completion. Included in this chapter are five idea Lists to help you set your goals and start working towards them. The five Lists are:

1. The **Mission Statement**
2. **Ideas for Resolutions** or Goals
3. **Goal Worksheet** or how to visualize each goal
4. **Monthly Goal Worksheet**, the small steps that lead to success
5. **Dreams to Dream / Places to See**

A few years ago, experts in organizational behavior started recommending mission statements for businesses so they would know where they were headed. Now this has filtered down to individuals who are compiling personal mission statements. In simple terms, you evaluate where you are now and contrast it with where you want to be. It's a deeper level than making resolutions since it extends far into the future and determines the path you want to follow. In the left-hand column you will finish each sentence to show where you are today. In the right-hand column you will plan where you want to be in the future. When it's all filled in, the right-hand column becomes your mission statement or how you want to develop throughout your life. There are no right answers, only your answers. You have successes which should be recognized in the left-hand column. Reward yourself by acknowledging your strengths when you write down your answers.

Two stipulations--be honest about what <u>you</u> want to do and determine your own dreams. And two, do not let the mountains obscure your vision--mountains such as fear, not enough education or no money. It's time to dream. Use as many pages as you need to complete the plan for your journey and don't limit yourself to the little boxes if you need room to grow.

MISSION STATEMENT

THIS IS WHERE I AM TODAY---	THIS IS WHERE I WANT TO BE IN THE FUTURE ---This is my Mission Statement
My mind has been focused on	Now my mind will be focused on:
My body has been controlled by:	Now my body will be:
In my early life I chose to:	I will modify my choice to include:
In the past I wanted to:	In the future I desire:
My time is spent doing:	My time will be spent:
Emotionally I have been:	My emotions now will focus on:
The barricades in my life have been:	To take down the barricades I will:
My relationship with those close to me:	My path with others will be:
A dream I had was to:	I would like to work on that dream by:
My service to others has been:	My service to others will be:
I have lost:	I want to find:
My main focus in life has been:	My main focus in life will be:
My fears have stopped me from:	By being courageous I will:

My idea of success has been:	Success is:
(Add your own special sentences)	

Change--this is about change with an eye to the horizon and beyond. Believe in yourself. Now rewrite these personal goals into a few sentences that summarize who you want to become and what you are working towards. Modify it as you gain knowledge about who you are.

My Mission Statement (summarized from above):

I Resolve To

The next List includes ideas for resolutions or goals. Some are simple and others require motivation and discipline at the deepest levels. Use this list to choose a goal or two. Then use the Goal Worksheet to plan how you are going to succeed at accomplishing this goal. Make this the year you work towards improving yourself and getting more organized.

Instructions: On the left side of the Resolutions List are ideas for goals. Go down the list and in the right columns **decide if this goal** is

#1 **Top Priority** this year,

#2 **Of Interest** to you but not as important, or

#3 **Not Of Interest** and is something you don't want to do.

After you've filled out those columns, go back and look at the #1 Top Priorities you have.

In the last column, **rank the Top Priorities** as to what is most important in your life. By process of elimination you probably have chosen your #1 goal for this year.

Go to Goal Worksheet and plan how you will complete this goal. If the goals are easy, you may accomplish many this year. If you pick a hard one, it may take you all year or a lifetime.

IDEAS FOR GOALS

This year, I resolve to:	Top Priority #1	Interested In #2	Not interested #3	Rank top priorities
TAKE CARE OF BODY BY:				
Start physical fitness program				
Meet with doctor, dentist, eye doctor				
Lose weight				
Stop smoking tobacco				
Give up harmful drugs				
Stop or limit alcoholic beverages				
Engage in athletics--solo or team				
Learn to dance, swim, backpack--get moving				
Improve body image				
TAKE CARE OF MIND BY:				
Read more books, newspapers				
Return for schooling--work towards degree or learning new technical skills				
Learn a foreign language				
Learn computer skills, Internet, etc.				
Learn web design / Start home page				
Learn to play musical instrument				
Join a choir, drama group, orchestra				
Research genealogy				
Take up painting, drawing, photography				
Write--fiction or non-fiction				
Cut back on watching television, time wasters				
GET ORGANIZED:				
Start using a planner, Palm Pilot, to-do-lists				
Clean out garage, closets, drawers-- Sort into trash / give to charity / clean & mend / keep				
Organize recipe files				
Organize photographs into albums or scrapbooks--names and dates on back				

This year, I resolve to:	Top Priority #1	Interested In #2	Not interested #3	Rank top priorities
Organize letters and keepsakes				
Print lists every month from List Organizer	Top Priority			
Organize whatever is out of control in my life				
RELATIONSHIPS:				
Make time for spouse, children, family				
Take parenting or marriage class				
Improve communications with friends, family				
Stop abuse in family				
Entertain				
Volunteer / Give service to others				
Forgive and forget				
EMPLOYMENT / CAREER:				
Make more money				
Review my job / Change jobs				
Go for career counseling				
Reduce or eliminate debt				
Learn investment / savings strategies				
Improve employment skills--training, classes				
Start new business				
PERSONAL:				
Start spiritual fitness program				
Take time for self				
Improve self-esteem and self-image				
Keep journal				
Meditate				
Travel				
Get rid of bad habit (swearing, temper, lying, procrastination, gossiping)				
Purchase item I've dreamed about (Auto, Furniture, Boat, Property)				

This year, I resolve to:	Top Priority #1	Interested In #2	Not interested #3	Rank top priorities
FUTURE--Prepare for:				
Marriage				
Addition to the family				
Graduation				
Divorce				
Retirement				
New home				
Moving				
YOUR SPECIAL DREAMS:				

History teaches us that even in the olden days people wanted to improve so they came up with the Seven Vices and the Seven Virtues. The idea was to get rid of the vices and change them to virtues. Many of our resolutions are still built on these.

The Virtues are Faith, Hope, Charity, Prudence, Justice, Temperance, and Fortitude.

The Vices are Lust, Envy, Sloth, Pride, Covet ness, Gluttony, and Anger.

GOAL WORKSHEET

!. Write down your goal—one per page   **HOW TO ACHIEVE YOUR GOAL # 1**

This year, I resolve to:

2. Step-It-Down--Come up with ten (more or less) steps you need to do to make this goal happen. 1.

2.
3.
4.
5.
6.
7.
8.
9.
10.

3. Time-It-Down--Schedule your steps. This is your timetable for the year so each step gets planned with a deadline date. Plan it by month using this worksheet or plan it by the week on your calendar or planning calendar. Use the Monthly Goal Worksheet each month.

January
February
March
April
May
June
July
August
September
October
November
December

4. Work-It-Out--Each day of the year. Look at this worksheet often. Work your schedule towards completion. Make it part of your successful thinking. Make It Happen. Follow Your Schedule. Stay motivated.

MONTHLY GOAL WORKSHEET

HOW TO ACHIEVE YOUR GOAL # 2

What you are going to do this month?

January, February, March, April, May, June, July, August, September, October, November, December (Print out 12 / Circle one for each month)

Step-It-Down--This is to help you consolidate your goal information into one area. On this list, combine every thing you are going to do for success this month. This information comes from all your Goal Worksheets and is a summary for this month.

1.

2.

3.

4.

5.

6.

7.

8.

9.

DREAMS to DREAM / PLACES to SEE

Everyone needs a few dreams. List them here. Also list places in the world you would like to visit including cities, museums, parks, buildings, etc. Dream on and make dreams become plans then reality. Use these as ideas for your goals.

☑	I Want To	What's Stopping You?	How Much Will It Cost?	Set A Date

CHAPTER FOUR

To Do Lists Make Those Dreams Come True

Time management has been treated as a complex, involved, process which requires massive numbers of people coordinating expansive amounts of information into hundreds of computers. Fortunately for you, I have been a mother of four small children, at home with only myself as a resource to develop a plan for managing an inexhaustible amount of requests, problems, and hungers.

From those years of struggle came List Organizer and how I learned to cope with time management in the home. In truth, it wasn't until the children became teenagers that I pulled together all the information and devised my own system. Also, it was the first time I had any free moments to write a book. Before that I tried to keep lists here and there and I scheduled our appointments and meetings. Yet the whole organization plan was not in place. It took years of trial and error to generate the force behind the chart and list system explained throughout the book.

Using lists to get organized confuses some people since they don't know what to do with a list that tells them how to clean a house. What are they supposed to do with all those sub-divided chores? Some people like "the pick and choose and do it now" system. When they have a few minutes, they look at the list and do one thing. When they have another spare minute, they work on another chore. Eventually they make a difference and the house starts to look better.

Some people are "the major house clean in one day" type of personality. They look at the same house maintenance list and get the family and friends involved to finish as many chores in one day as possible. They like to see an immediate difference in the house because of their effort. If those styles work for you, then go ahead and keep track of house cleaning from the **House Maintenance List**. The Lists may be used successfully with either of those approaches.

My style requires a different tactic since I need a long-range plan so I don't get confused and become frustrated with ideas for so many unfinished everyday jobs in my head. I like to consolidate all those sub-divided chores onto two summary sheets that help me develop a plan. Without a plan, I start to feel I can never get ahead since I'm so far behind. With the help of two Lists, I avoid this pitfall.

The first is the **Monthly To-Do List** with fourteen boxes each topped with a category that corresponds to parts of personal life. One page represents one month of the year and for every year I copy twelve sheets ready to be filled in and stored in my planning binder. For example, I use the **Household Maintenance List** and decide which chores need to be completed during the next year. Some of the chores don't apply to me and I ignore them. Then I transfer those chores onto a Monthly To-Do List under the category Household Maintenance.

To schedule "turn the mattresses on the beds" to preserve their life, I decide how often to do that and I choose every three months. With my **Monthly To-Do Lists** I write down "Turn

Mattresses" on each of the March / June / September / December Lists which schedules that chore every three months.

Next I see "Wash shower curtains" and decide to do that every six months. Then I choose other months that aren't too busy and write down that chore in February / August and I'll remember to do that every six months. On Page 30 is your copy of the **Monthly To-Do List**. There are twelve pages for January through December, but you can start using them in any month of the year

To use my system, copy twelve of the **Monthly To-Do Lists** and fill them in using some of the Lists later in the book. It's so simple that you don't need to plan every part of your life Maybe you want to plan your Meals or Clothing Care and won't bother with the rest of the categories that are listed. Under body care you might schedule a manicure or a facial or that monthly trip to the beauty or barber shop. Schedule a vacation for May and a trip to the amusement park in July. Dream a little when you make plans. It's not all drudgery.

Schedule that oil change every few months for your automobile or plan your garden planting or thinning in certain months. This list is a blueprint of some of the things you will be doing in that month. If you need more room use the back of the List.

Example: Your 12 pages may include some chores to be done once every month, such as wash the dog. List, "Wash the dog" on all 12 pages since it needs to be done every month.

You may have something that needs to be done every other month. List that chore on 6 of the monthly pages, skipping a month between.
Example: January, March, May, July, September, November

A chore to be done 4 times a year will be listed on 4 monthly pages with two months between.
Example: February, May, August, November

Twice yearly chores will be listed on two monthly pages with five months between. Example: March, September

And a yearly chore will be listed only on one page.

How do you decide which months get which chores? Guess work is the answer. For example, it is nice to have your silverware polished and ready for Thanksgiving dinner. Polishing the silverware can be scheduled in October or November to plan ahead. Spend a little time visualizing what you do in each month of the year. Think about your schedule when children are home for summer vacation, or when relatives usually visit, or when your work schedule is tightest, or when the holidays are approaching. In your visualizing you will know when you have the most available time and when time is limited.

Schedule your chores around your year. These dates are not written in granite. You may change as the time comes closer and you see that a certain date will not be convenient. Always, reschedule the activity to another month.

MONTHLY TO-DO LIST

Fill in chores you want to accomplish this month

January, February, March, April, May, June, July, August, September, October, November, December
(Circle one for each month)

☑	HOUSEHOLD MAINTENANCE	☑	FINANCIAL
☑	CLOTHING AND ACCESSORIES	☑	PERSONAL CARE / BODY CARE
☑	EMPLOYMENT / SCHOOL	☑	HEALTH / MEDICAL / DENTAL
☑	MEAL PLANNING / FOOD	☑	GIFTS / CARDS / LETTERS
☑	CHILD CARE / PETS	☑	GARDENING / LAWN / PLANTS
☑	ENTERTAINING / HOLIDAYS	☑	VACATION / ACTIVITIES
☑	VEHICLE MAINTENANCE.	☑	MISCELLANEOUS

Prioritize chores. Check off when completed.

The second List I use is a **Weekly To-Do List**. Let me say right now that I don't use a Daily To-Do List since I kept failing at getting things done and then I went into failure mode with a daily list giving me only 24 hours to finish everything. I do believe in a calendar to schedule my 24 hours of time, but that subject will be covered in Chapter 5.

The **Weekly To-Do List** is similar to a daily list only it gives me 168 hours to complete everything on the list. I like the possibility that I can get most of the things completed by the end of the week in my 168 hours of work time. Most people seem to know how to put together a short daily list and they are wonderful for short term goals, but many times they set you up for failure on your long term chores.

When you mention "A List" the "To-Do" list is what most people think about. This is where you keep track of everything you need to do with your time and then you check off each one as it's completed. It's a basic list that has been around for years. We may have learned to prioritize them and color-code them, but the idea is still the same--to get everything out of your head and onto a piece of paper or Palm Pilot or computer program.

One day a week, plan what you want to get done during the next week under each category. This gives you a place to transfer lots of those goals and chores you have from other lists in the book.

The website, www.listorganizer.com contains Monthly Lists with the current dated month. I also offer the Weekly To-Do List and the Weekly To-Do Dated Lists that are four separate lists, one with the date for each of the coming weeks. You may use these Lists if you don't want to copy the Monthly and Weekly To-Do Lists.

Keep marking chores off whether on your weekly or monthly list. Keep transferring uncompleted items to your next weekly or monthly list. You may use the back of your printed list for writing delegation plans for who is going to help you with all those chores. Or just use it to add your own categories. Sometimes there's too much work and you need to delegate. Use the **Honey Do** list contained in this book for your spouse or the **Delegation** list for children and others.

Using a Weekly List gives you seven days to complete an item or thirty days for your Monthly List. This extra time sets you up for success. It doesn't matter if you don't finish on Tuesday or whatever day. You have the rest of the week to try again.

Some adults, for example those with ADD or struggling with depression, need a Daily list of basic things to do each day. You may make your own by using the **Personal Care** list to help remember things you need to do for your body.

If you think you will hyperventilate if you don't have a daily to-do list, jot down items on a wipe off board or in your planning calendar or even on a single piece of paper and have the satisfaction or crossing those off each day. At least give yourself a chance with maybe a Three Day Chore List that adds 72 hours to your completion time. I still like the Weekly and Monthly Lists since they give you more time to succeed.

Children need a daily list since their brains haven't learned the automatic daily chores. Use the **Daily or Weekly Child's To-Do** List. Children need the satisfaction of accomplishing small goals each day. These simple chores will help them build confidence towards longer term goals. Check out the **Ideas for Child's Chores** and the **Bedroom Clean up Chart**.

Gradually, you will learn to schedule your weekly chores by jotting them down on the **Weekly To-Do List**. To schedule a week you need to be open-minded and make some educated predictions. After you complete a weekly chore and mark it off on your calendar, you may want to reschedule it for next week. Soon you will see a pattern in some chores that you do every week and they will become so automatic that you won't need to write them down anymore. Your brain has taken over and remembers that you are going to vacuum every week and water the plants. Then you have succeeded in making that part of your repeated weekly routine.

Not Enough Time

Wait! You wanted to vacuum twice a week and the only day you might be able to do that is Saturday? Then you have to change your expectations about how much time you have to give each chore. Write down "Vacuum" on your Monthly To-Do List instead and see if you can manage it during the month. Even though your rugs may look bad by the time you get to them, you may have to accept your limitations. You can add another "Vacuum" day when your time permits. At least you are completing this chore once in a while and you don't have to worry about it anymore.

Or you really need to pay your bills every two weeks but it's been sliding into four weeks and your financial life is a mess. Try to schedule "Pay the Bills" every two weeks and see if it works for you. If not, schedule that chore every three weeks. And finally, put it on the Monthly To-Do List and make sure it gets done at least once a month. Flexibility in the system makes it easy to change at any time.

As you look at your Weekly To-Do List, prioritize tasks in order of importance so you don't end up with overdue bills and no food in the house while your house looks great. Successful time management is a process of concentrating on the most important items in your life, completing those, and moving on to complete other chores that are vital but not critical.

I consider six areas of life very important to organize. They are:
- Body care, with a regular routine
- Financial since it affects so many areas of your life
- Food, meals and menus since you can't put off daily nourishment
- Clothing care including laundry and upkeep and closet organization
- Child care takes priority and includes grandparents still concerned about children
- Household maintenance to make home a pleasurable place
- Add education if you are in school

WEEKLY TO-DO LIST

Fill in the chores you want to accomplish this week (Date)_____

☑	HOUSEHOLD MAINTENANCE	☑	FOOD
☑	CLOTHING AND ACCESSORIES	☑	PERSONAL CARE
☑	FINANCIAL	☑	MAIL / CORRESPONDENCE
☑	CHILD CARE	☑	EMPLOYMENT / SCHOOL
☑	HEALTH / MEDICAL / DENTAL	☑	PETS AND PLANTS
☑	MISCELLANEOUS	☑	ODDS AND ENDS

Prioritize chores—what is most important to complete. Check off when completed. These Lists have amazing power to control your time and transform your organization habits. And time is the stuff of which your life is made.

CHAPTER FIVE

Why Do I Need a Calendar If I Have a To-Do List?

The charts and lists in this book are the heart of the personalized planning system. Yet you still need a planning calendar, as the head or mind to keep track of your schedules. You need a place to keep track of where you belong at what time along with others who require your help to get to their appointments.

A planning system is a powerful time management tool and it can successfully organize your personal life which may be a new concept for you. Most office executives and their secretaries rely heavily on an office appointment and planning book. To manage a personal life, people also need a system for putting together all the parts of life management.

A calendar is similar to an appointment book. A calendar takes all that information floating around in your brain and puts it on paper. That means you can stop worrying about everything you might have forgotten. That includes items such as meetings, health care professional appointments, parties, athletic competitions and practices, and get-togethers with other people. The majority of adults manage to write down telephone messages and appointments on their calendars so they don't miss important events.

Don't be afraid when I mention having to start a planning or scheduling calendar. You can gently slide into this instead of becoming a minute-by-minute time fanatic. You will not be required to handcuff this planner to your wrist and carry it with you to sporting events, dinner parties or on vacation. Time management is meant to help you. The plan will give you freedom instead of giving you something else to worry about. You will be the master of the system and not the other way around.

Some people are going to pass up the instructions given in Chapter 4 about using To-Do Lists to plan chores. You are more comfortable using your paper planner or PDA as a scheduler plus a summary for the chores you want to do. Great! Instead of experimenting with my Monthly and Weekly To-Do Lists, keep track of that same information in your planner or on your PDA. For many years I used a paper planner in a binder to keep track of my monthly chores and it performed well. That method helped me get a good routine established for personal organization.

Many of the yearly calendars include monthly pages to track your monthly chores. Plus you can use other pages to plan your weekly chores. In using this method remember to

1. Check off each item as it's completed. This not only tells you it's done but that checkmark sends a signal that you have succeeded in organizing part of your life.
2. Prioritize the chores so the most important things are completed in order.

A planning system is similar to a calendar except it includes more space for recording appointments, to-do-lists and expenses. It may include goal setting pages, address pages, or a diary page. It is more comprehensive than a calendar. It may be housed in leather or vinyl; a three-ring format or a spiral; zippered or open. Your local office supply store, major discount store, and college bookstore sell planning systems.

People are carrying organizers and using them in offices, schools, grocery stores and homes. Open your eyes and you will discover how many people own and use these planners. Talk to these organized human beings and get their opinions on what they like and dislike about their planners or PDAs. Browse through your local stores and note the types and styles of calendars you prefer. The best kind is the pre-dated type so you do not have to fill in the dates.

Written planners today are available in many formats: two-pages a week, two-pages a day, one-page a day, or a month at a glance. You may purchase pages with a large appointment space and a smaller to-do space or just the reverse. The planners are varied enough you can find one perfect for your needs. I suggest you purchase an inexpensive starter calendar. Then if it does not fit your needs, you won't feel devastated about junking it and changing to another system.

You must guess how much space you are going to need to write down your weekly and monthly responsibilities and to schedule appointments. Some people try one size planner, find it not to their liking, and change to a larger or smaller calendar next year. A common problem among first time planning system users is the size of the pages is either too big or small for their scheduling needs. Tastes vary from purse size to briefcase size planners.

Remember, you can convert to another system if you cannot live with the planner you have chosen. So arrive at an educated guess and make a purchase. Do not become so bogged down looking for the perfect planner that you never get around to planning your time because you cannot decide the best planning book for you.

Warning #1: Do not buy a very small calendar. You will have the plan halfway recorded for your year, and find out you do not have enough space to record your selected chores. This is enough to make anyone throw up their hands and quit.

Warning #2: Do not buy an expensive system with the leather binding and all the gadgets that go with it until you are sure it is the best system for you. It is money thrown away if you find you hate the expensive planner you spent too much money to obtain.

Perhaps you would like to ask me, "What planning system do you use? I teach workshops in how to use this system and that question is often asked. I used to be very specific and tell participants exactly which planner I used. After they purchased it and tried my style of planner, they did not like it, wanted a different size or format and sent it back.

Now I let you do a little work and decide for yourself what planner or calendar is superior for you. You will probably be happier with your choice.

Formatting a Calendar

The skeptic is now starting to add up how much time it is going to take to organize his time. He may give up reading since it seems to be too much trouble. Wrong (and right.) To be honest, the initial setup of your planning system does require time. However, since it is done at your pace and according to your schedule, it never becomes too much work. It does necessitate some time and commitment from each individual. I cannot come to help you setup your own system, so I have simplified it and you can do it with a little effort.

The charts and lists will be a guide for you, but you need to decide if you really have time to complete all these chores. To use the system as I've described it, you need to take the information from each List and transfer it to either the **Monthly and Weekly To-Do Lists** or your calendar whichever you've selected as the method you prefer. Then once it is written, the maintenance of the calendar is easy and needs only a rescheduling moment when chores are completed.

Many of the Lists do not require you to schedule anything such as the Lists that tell you what to take Shopping or on a Hike or to Work. You just use those as is and don't need to schedule those. Other Lists, such as the **Personal Care**, **Household Maintenance** or **Vehicle Maintenance** Lists give you ideas that may be planned ahead. For example, the chores on **Household Maintenance** may be scheduled on your calendar. **Grocery Lists** are not scheduled but the trip to the grocery store might be put on your Weekly List.

Many Lists are reminders of items to buy or pack and do not have to be scheduled. However, time to buy items on the lists or time to pack might be scheduled. In the final count of time wasted and time used wisely, the more planning you can do, the more time you will find you have.

When you go to the store and have planned what to buy, you do not waste as much time running up and down aisles, looking at the shelves and trying to see if you meant to buy any of those products. You combine chores so they are done in a sequence that saves time. You group stores to be visited so when you head into town, you know where you have to go and what other store nearby needs to be visited also by taking along the **Places I Need To Go** List.

These ideas have been around for years. Time managers have told us to group chores and keep lists and prioritize "things to do" for years. So why do people have trouble connecting these ideas together?

My theory is that not enough of our plans are written in one place to make it efficient. So we need these summary sheets such as my To-Do Lists or a calendar, planner or PDA which stores masses of personal information in an easy to use format.

In summary, you are welcome to use the Lists in one of three ways:

1. Make up your own individual system, fill in the Lists and check off the sub-divided parts in your own way, at your own speed.
2. Use my complete system with Monthly and Weekly To-Do Lists for planning chores taken from the Lists. That includes a calendar for scheduling appointments and also using other Lists that are free-standing and don't need to have their sub-divided chores grouped onto the summary sheets.
3. Use a calendar, planner or PDA for planning and scheduling your life including the sub-divided chores from the Lists.

As long as you find success with this personalized planning system, the journey and the tools you use to achieve your goals are not important. The only part that is critical to success is the Lists and the power they will give to you.

CHAPTER SIX

What Goes in All Those Boxes on the To Do Lists?

People see those empty To-Do Lists and don't know what to do with them. I made this List with suggestions for basic time management and to give you a weekly view of where your time goes. It helps you figure out why you are so busy and rushed. It will show you why you can't fit in another activity or it helps you eliminate activities so you can have recreation and leisure. It's a simple tool that helps you see that life is filled with more than scheduled activities. This is planning when you don't know where to start.

Start with this List to make your own To-Do-List. What do you want to organize this week? What habit are you going to work on this week? Get some new ideas

Everyone needs a weekly plan and a monthly plan. Call it goal setting or simply thinking ahead. Some days are busier than other days. Some days are the same as the day before. You choose. What will you work on during a typical week?

On the next page are some suggestions for personal goals. They have to do with organizing yourself and your priorities. Put a check mark in the days you want to work on your various projects. Remember, just because you plan to balance your checkbook on Monday doesn't mean it has to be done that day unless it's critical. According to my rule, you have a week to complete your planned chores that are flexible. Some chores are rigid and have to be done on certain days and we all live with those responsibilities. You have to show up to your employment on the days you are scheduled.

- Transfer the chores you've marked onto your To-Do Lists (Weekly or Monthly) then just glance at your To-Do lists each day to see where your priorities are.
- You may want to prioritize the chores with numbers 1, 2, 3 etc. instead of just marking them This is as close to a Daily List as we get since you complete the #1s before moving on to other items.
- If a chore doesn't have to be scheduled on a specific day, put a check mark in the last column (Week) to indicate you will find time to do it sometime during your busy 168 available weekly hours.

PERSONAL CARE

WHAT I HAVE TO WORK ON THIS WEEK	Monday	Tuesday	Wednesday	Thursday	Friday	Saturday	Sunday	Week
Auto maintenance								
Banking at home or off to the bank								
Bills--pay around payday Use Budget Lists								
Briefcase, handbag, backpack--clean								
Calendars, change								
Calendar, plan								
Car pool-what days do you have one								
Checkbook, balance								
Child care at home or day care								
Clothes to dry cleaners								
Clothes to iron								
Clothes, do laundry								
Clothes, plan what to wear								
Clothes / shoes repair and mend								
Correspondence and greeting cards to send								
Coupons to clip and organize								
Employment--which days do you work								
Entertain--fun with friends and family								
Exercise								
File your bills and papers								
Files, maintain your personal and family files								
Financial--establish and maintain your budget								
Financial records, organize and maintain								
Gifts--purchase and wrap								
Greeting cards--birthdays, anniversaries, etc.								
Grocery shopping								
Grooming--manicure, color hair, facial, etc.								
Hobby--make time for this								
Holiday--plan for holiday entertaining / decorating / etc.								
Household maintenance								
Houseplants--fertilize and prune and water								

WHAT I HAVE TO WORK ON THIS WEEK	Monday	Tuesday	Wednesday	Thursday	Friday	Saturday	Sunday	Week
Insurance--forms to fill out								
Journal--write your life story								
Leisure--take time for relaxation								
Mail--incoming and outgoing								
Meal planning								
Meal preparation and clean up								
Medical appointments--dental, eye, medical								
Pet care--feeding plus extra baths								
Photographs--develop film and organize photos								
Prescriptions, refill								
Reading--time for book/ magazine								
School--classes and homework and research								
Sports--time for recreation								
Telephone calls								
Vacation--see Travel								

I Have a To Do List—What Next?

Outstanding! You have scheduled your first Monthly or Weekly To-Do List or you've scheduled some chores on your PDA. What do you do with all that wonderful information that is now scheduled?

1. Look at the Weekly To-Do List each day.

2. Assign priorities as to what is most important to be done first, second, etc., for that day.

3. Complete the work (or delegate the work).

4. Try again tomorrow or next month as you reschedule what does not get done.

Then if it is a good day and you have extra time, check the Monthly-To-Do chart for the current month and see what you could complete in the time you have available.

We both know you are going to have days when the work does not get completed so we will allow for realism here. There will be bad days when time gets away from you and you will skip some chores and reschedule others. No problem. Remember, you have a week to complete your List.

Rotate Forward or Defer

You got sick, the dog threw up on the carpet, your car battery died and you have unexpected houseguests. Your schedule is shot and you are starting to feel ashamed about how unorganized you are. Settle down. You are going to reschedule the important chores and let some others slide until life is under control again. This is called Rotate Forward or Defer. Whatever did not get accomplished gets rescheduled to a new date in the future.

When April becomes a day of allergy attacks instead of housecleaning, reschedule those household chores onto the May monthly page. When May brings extra gardening and not as much time for the household chores, keep as many chores on the May list as possible and reschedule the others to June or July or August.

Are your guilt hormones speaking up and saying you are not allowed to do that because it indicates procrastination or delay tactics? Not really. The chores are done eventually because they are on the schedule. This may be a new concept for some of you that you are allowed to organize and reschedule your own time. Get used to that "take charge feeling" since the only way to make an organization system work is to allow for problems and personalities to adapt when catastrophe hits and plans change. Rotate forward and reschedule.

Delegation

At some point after you have rescheduled: "Wash the windows", 12 times, you may have to admit that you are not going to complete that chore. That doesn't mean it won't get done. You need another possible choice called Delegation.

In business, people who delegate are praised highly for their ability to get others to work for them and to accomplish more because they are leaders. In personal life we think that delegation means defeat. You need to change your thinking and pay someone to do that job for you. Learn to delegate.

Delegate to your spouse, to your children, to a neighbor, or to paid, hired help. Be specific about the chore and when it needs to be done. You may negotiate a payment or you may negotiate a swap in labor. The payment may be money, or it might mean you help your assistant with another task when you have extra time. The two Lists below are for delegation to others. One is a **Honey Do List**. The second **Delegation List** is for children, family, or friends

Honey, I do love you. Please find time to help me with the following chores.

☑	CHORES THAT NEED TO BE COMPLETED	SUN	MON	TUES	WED	THUR	FRI	SAT

Check the days of the week when you need this done. Let your helper check off the left hand column when the chore is completed.

Thank you for helping me. Please find time to help me with the following chores on the days I have checked.

☑	CHORES THAT NEED TO BE COMPLETED	SUN	MON	TUES	WED	THUR	FRI	SAT

Sometimes you will put chores on your list that sounded marvelous at the time, but now you realize you are not concerned if that errand is completed. Instead of rescheduling a chore, drop it off the list. It is part of a cycle I call

- Defer
- Delegate
- Delete

Now you have learned about deferring the items or rotating them forward to be done in the future and rescheduling. Also you learned about delegation and how you can't do all the work yourself.

Delete is exactly what it means—it gets rid of your sub-divided chore because you aren't going to do it and you aren't going to delegate it so it causes a guilty conscience. Instead of feeling guilty about never completing some chores, erase them from your plan. If it bothers you to let it go, you may keep a list in your planner of what assignments you are omitting so you may pick them up in a year when time permits.

Perfectionist Planning and Rescheduling

There are some people among us who are perfectionists and they love the thought of being totally organized. I have included this section for them. It explains how to keep your To-Do Lists and calendar in a state of never-ending flawlessness

Each day when a chore is completed, get in the habit of rotating it forward to another line on a future Weekly or Monthly To-Do Lists. A weekly chore that is scheduled once a week will be moved ahead to the next week. By rescheduling the chores to the next week or month or year when it needs to be done again, your calendar is updated and never needs to be initially setup again. If you forget to do this, your planning calendar will stop because no tasks will be rescheduled. Some people don't mind this and make up a Weekly List on the fly by looking at last week, glancing at the Lists in the book and trying to remember what to do. Perfectionists cannot do this. Non-perfectionists seem to have no trouble being a little more casual with their plan.

"Oh, my gosh!" you exclaim. I think I forgot to reschedule 'Pick up the prescriptions' last month and now I cannot remember when it needs to be done." Sometimes you forget to rotate forward and reschedule. Since you have your written notation on last month's calendar, you can refer backwards to the previous month to pick up your forgotten chore. This written planner never forgets when you actually accomplished an errand. It is there to help you shift tasks forward.

Flip backwards through last month's To-Do List or the listing on your PDA and find the day when you last had the prescriptions refilled. Quickly examine your summary sheet (either the To-Do Lists or your own planner or PDA) and recalculate when the chore needs to be repeated. Reschedule the chore.

Chores need to be repeated over and over. The planning system allows you constantly to keep ahead of the chores since you reschedule them each time they are marked off as completed. Mark off a chore as it is completed and reschedule it in the future. It may take you a while to recall this important process.

Mark Off a completed chore;
Rotate Forward and
Reschedule it on another day to be repeated.

When you remember this process, your calendar is not hard to maintain since it is being updated daily. Plan to spend a few vital minutes with your calendar when convenient to revise and reschedule chores. It's easy to pick up this system again if you take a break so don't worry if you go on vacation or get sick or get lazy. Start again making a new To-Do List.

Summary

Chapter 3-- gave you Lists for direction, how to set goals and follow through.
Chapter 4-- taught you about the importance of To-Do Lists, Monthly and Weekly
Chapter 5-- showed you why you need a calendar to schedule events in your life
Chapter 6-- gave you ideas how to fill in the Monthly and Weekly To-Do Lists

CHAPTER SEVEN

Where Should I Keep My Planning Lists?

The best place to store your To-Do Lists or your calendar depends on your home and office setup. Since this is an organization system for your personal life, the calendar probably should be kept in your home. This is an easy decision for those people who work at home--it stays at home with them in a safe place.

Commuters need to make a choice: Are you going to schedule your office appointments in the same calendar with your personal appointments and To-Do charts?

A "Yes" answer, you are going to use the same calendar for both personal and office scheduling, means the calendar has to go back and forth between home and office since it needs to be at both places. This can be complicated since there may be times when the calendar gets left at the wrong place in an emergency. Some people take their calendar with them every place and use it as a diary in addition to using it as a planner. Those people seldom forget to pick up the planner and take it along every day since it gets tucked into a briefcase or purse.

A "Yes" answer for disorganized people who forget where the planner is buried on their desk may mean buying two calendars: one for home and one for work. It is a little more trouble, but the peace of mind of having the right calendar in the right place at the essential time is worth the trouble. The calendar you need for this system will stay at home. People who keep their planner at home have to decide whether to take it with them to stores, library, doctor's offices, etc.

What To Do When Your Calendar Is Not With You

Buy a pad of small, sticky note paper. Keep this pad in your wallet, purse, automobile, or another place that is usually with you wherever you travel. This little pad of paper helps you when your calendar is at home or the office and you need to remember a name, an address, an appointment, the title of a book you want to read, the name of a medication, etc.

When your calendar is not handy, you can write down the information on these pieces of paper. When you return to the location of your calendar, either transfer the information onto the calendar or simply stick the reminder in the appropriate place.

For example, you make a return appointment at the dentist's office and need to confirm it with your calendar at home. Write down the information on a page of your small, paper in your purse or wallet. Check on the calendar when you return home. If the appointment was arranged at a convenient time, transfer the information onto your calendar or put the piece of paper in the calendar on that date. When the appointment conflicts with another commitment, call the dentist and reschedule the appointment.

Planning is only one step. Make sure you do the work and mark it off (reschedule) as the days fly by.

Mark Off--Rotate Forward—Reschedule

Final Instructions

You should know by now that every part of your life may never be organized. Life is complex. It is difficult to work at a full-time job, maintain a spotless house while raising children, entertain weekly, keep a yard full of fed and brushed pets, keep everything growing in the greenhouse and keep dirt off the car.

Instead of thinking of this system as an excuse for being lazy and letting certain tasks go, I think of it as being realistic and planning for the time I have available in my waking hours. There are days when you might visit my home and the house would not be spotless. But the work is scheduled to be done and I am able to keep up with my commitments. My car may not always be vacuumed, but it is scheduled once a month and maybe in the middle of bad weather when the snow has tracked in, I haven't been able to fit in an extra day to vacuum the car.

It doesn't bother me anymore. My standards are similar to my old standards. However, now I schedule the work and do the work when it is scheduled. I don't try to be spontaneous and wake up each morning trying to figure out what I need to do. I know what I need to do. It is listed on my Weekly To-Do List, my Monthly To-Do List and my calendar.

Telephone calls and appointments are recorded on my calendar. Any important items are added if I feel they merit my attention. Otherwise, I let some things go. And I reassess my requirements every four months. Some items are dropped and some are added. Finally, I feel my life belongs to me instead of my calendar or my home or my volunteer work or my job. It's amazing to me that I now have more time for my family and me since I schedule time for that also. Enjoy your life. Take control in your own way.

Section Two

The Lists

Time + Lists = POWER

THE POWER OF LISTS

Now you enter the part of the book that contains the Power of Lists. The remaining pages contain dozens of Lists, sub-divided and pre-made for you to use. The Lists allow you to make up your own Personalized Planning System just as if a professional organizer had come to your house and evaluated your life.

After working with clients for ten years, I've compiled the Lists that have benefited them and will benefit you. With a little reading, you will find the Lists that are most important to you. I recommend you start organizing the important six parts of life I listed in Chapter 4. Since it's your personal system, you can start wherever you like.

I'm excited to turn over this information to you. It will make a difference in your life as your change old habits and develop a new way of life. Remember this does involve change and forming new habits which is difficult. With a little motivation, you can change a little this week and next month until the change becomes easy and your kitchen is clean and your closet is organized and you didn't feel any pain.

Don't quit. I repeat myself by telling you again --time is the stuff of which your life is made. Don't squander it in a mess of clutter and disorganization. You were meant for better things. Shine on as you discover your gift for getting organized.

The first Lists are personal information about you such as vital information, financial information and medical information. Keep this information in a secure place that could be accessed by family and friends if needed but kept hidden from strangers. There are two styles of Lists and you may fill out both of them or chose the own that fits your lifestyle. Many times I include more than one List for the same subject. You choose the one that meets your needs.

Personal Information Section Includes These Lists:

PERSONAL AND FAMILY INFORMATION # 1 & 2

FINANCIAL INFORMATION # 1 & 2

CREDIT CARD ACCOUNTS

MEDICAL INFORMATION # 1 & 2

TAKING CARE OF YOUR BODY

PERSONAL AND FAMILY INFORMATION #1

FIRST NAME	NICKNAME	**LAST NAME**
STREET ADDRESS	CITY, STATE	ZIP
HOME TELEPHONE	CELL TELEPHONE	E-MAIL
BIRTH DATE	PLACE OF BIRTH	SOCIAL SECURITY # (IDENTIFICATION #)
DRIVER'S LICENSE #	EXPIRATION DATE	
NAME OF MOTHER / PLACE OF BIRTH	NAME OF FATHER / PLACE OF BIRTH	BROTHERS & SISTERS
NAME OF SPOUSE	MARRIAGE DATE / PLACE	SPOUSE BIRTH DATE / PLACE
CHILD'S NAME / BIRTH DATE / PLACE	CHILD'S NAME / BIRTH DATE / PLACE	CHILD'S NAME / BIRTH DATE / PLACE
CHILD'S NAME / BIRTH DATE / PLACE	CHILD'S NAME / BIRTH DATE / PLACE	CHILD'S NAME / BIRTH DATE / PLACE
YOUR EDUCATION / SCHOOLS ATTENDED	DEGREES EARNED	HONORS
EMPLOYMENT:		
MILITARY SERVICE:	RELIGIOUS AFFILIATION:	TALENTS / HOBBIES:

Keep this in a secure place where it won't be stolen.

PERSONAL INFORMATION #2

Name: _____

Social Security number: _____

Date of birth:_____ Place of birth:_____

Current Marriage:

Spouse's name_____

Spouse's birth date_____ Place of birth:_____

Date of marriage_____ Place of marriage:_____

Children:

1. Name:_____ Sex:_____

   Date of birth:_____ Place of birth:_____

2. Name:_____ Sex:_____

   Date of birth:_____ Place of birth:_____

3. Name:_____ Sex:_____

   Date of birth:_____ Place of birth:_____

4. Name:_____ Sex:_____

   Date of birth:_____ Place of birth:_____

5. Name:_____ Sex:_____

   Date of birth:_____ Place of birth:_____

6. Name:_____ Sex:_____

   Date of birth:_____ Place of birth:_____

LISTS FOR MUDDLE MANAGEMENT

Previous marriage:

Spouse's name_____

Spouse's birth date_____   Place of birth:_____

Date of marriage_____   Place of marriage:_____

Date of death_____   Place of death_____

Date of divorce_____   Place of divorce_____

ADDRESSES WHERE I HAVE LIVED

1. Current Address_____

    City and State_____

    Resided from date _____ To_____

    Marital status_____ Employer_____

2. Current Address_____

    City and State_____

    Resided from date _____ To_____

    Marital status_____ Employer_____

3 Current Address_____

    City and State_____

    Resided from date _____ To_____

    Marital status_____ Employer_____

4 Current Address_____

    City and State_____

    Resided from date _____ To_____

    Marital status_____ Employer_____

You choose: fill in the information on List #1, or List #2 or both.

FINANCIAL INFORMATION #1

1. ISSUER OF CREDIT CARD	ADDRESS	TELEPHONE NUMBER
CREDIT CARD #	EXPIRATION DATE	CREDIT LIMIT / CUT OFF DATE
2. ISSUER OF CREDIT CARD	ADDRESS	TELEPHONE NUMBER
CREDIT CARD #	EXPIRATION DATE	CREDIT LIMIT / CUT OFF DATE
3. ISSUER OF CREDIT CARD	ADDRESS	TELEPHONE NUMBER
CREDIT CARD #	EXPIRATION DATE	CREDIT LIMIT / CUT OFF DATE
NAME OF BANK (CHECKING ACCOUNT)	ADDRESS	TELEPHONE NUMBER
ACCOUNT # (KEEP PIN # IN SEPARATE LOCATION)	NAMES ON ACCOUNT	
NAME OF BANK (SAVINGS ACCOUNT)	ADDRESS	TELEPHONE NUMBER
ACCOUNT #	NAMES ON ACCOUNT	
NAME OF BROKER / INTERNET ACCOUNT COMPANY	ACCOUNT NUMBER	LOCATION OF STATEMENTS / REPORTS
TYPE OF INVESTMENT	NAMES ON ACCOUNT	FUND NUMBER

TYPE OF INVESTMENT	NAMES ON ACCOUNT	FUND NUMBER
TYPE OF INVESTMENT	NAMES ON ACCOUNT	FUND NUMBER
TYPE OF INVESTMENT	NAMES ON ACCOUNT	FUND NUMBER
TYPE OF INVESTMENT	NAMES ON ACCOUNT	FUND NUMBER
SAFE DEPOSIT BOX LOCATION	BOX #	LOCATION OF KEY
ITEM IN SAFE DEPOSIT BOX:	VALUE	
ITEM IN SAFE DEPOSIT BOX:	VALUE	
ITEM IN SAFE DEPOSIT BOX:	VALUE	
ITEM IN SAFE DEPOSIT BOX:	VALUE	
ITEM IN SAFE DEPOSIT BOX:	VALUE	
ITEM IN SAFE DEPOSIT BOX:	VALUE	
LOCATION OF FINANCIAL RECORDS	LOCATION OF PERSONAL RECORDS	LOCATION OF ESTATE INFORMATION
LOCATION OF INSURANCE RECORDS	LOCATION OF RETIREMENT RECORDS	

Keep this information in a secure location--you don't want it stolen. Keep your Internet passwords and bank PIN #'s separate from this List.

FINANCIAL INFORMATION #2

BANK/SAVINGS AND LOAN ACCOUNTS

1. Bank name_____

   Bank address_____

   Date opened_____ Date closed_____

   Account type_____ Account number_____

2. Bank name_____

   Bank address_____

   Date opened_____ Date closed_____

   Account type_____ Account number_____

3. Bank name_____

   Bank address_____

   Date opened_____ Date closed_____

   Account type_____ Account number_____

4. Bank name_____

   Bank address_____

   Date opened_____ Date closed_____

   Account type_____ Account number_____

5. Bank name_____

   Bank address_____

   Date opened_____ Date closed_____

   Account type_____ Account number_____

CREDIT CARD ACCOUNTS

1. Card type_____ Card number_____

    Issued by: Name_____

    Address_____% Rate_____

    Telephone #_____ Expiration date_____

2. Card type_____ Card number_____

    Issued by: Name_____

    Address_____% Rate_____

    Telephone #_____ Expiration date_____

3. Card type_____ Card number_____

    Issued by: Name_____

    Address_____% Rate_____

    Telephone #_____ Expiration date_____

4. Card type_____ Card number_____

    Issued by: Name_____

    Address_____% Rate_____

    Telephone #_____ Expiration date_____

5. Card type_____ Card number_____

    Issued by: Name_____

    Address_____% Rate_____

    Telephone #_____ Expiration date_____

MEDICAL INFORMATION #1

FIRST NAME	NICKNAME	**LAST NAME**
STREET ADDRESS	CITY, STATE, ZIP	HOME TELEPHONE
BIRTH DATE	PLACE OF BIRTH	HEIGHT & WEIGHT
BLOOD TYPE	MEDICATION ALLERGIES	FOOD ALLERGIES
PHARMACIST & TELEPHONE #	CURRENT MEDICATIONS / DOSAGE	
PRIMARY CARE PHYSICIAN	PHYSICIAN ADDRESS	PHYSICIAN TELEPHONE #
SPECIALIST	SPECIALIST ADDRESS	SPECIALIST TELEPHONE #
OPTOMETRIST	OPTOMETRIST ADDRESS	OPTOMETRIST TELEPHONE #
DENTIST	DENTIST ADDRESS	DENTIST TELEPHONE #
HEALTH INSURANCE NAME / ADDRESS	TELEPHONE #	POLICY NUMBER

IMMUNIZATION DATES: CHICKEN POX	DPT	HEPATITIS B
MEASLES / MUMPS/ RUBELLA	PNEUMONIA	POLIO
SMALL POX	TETANUS	TUBERCULOSIS
OTHER (FLU)		
HOSPITALIZATIONS / SURGERIES		
ILLNESSES / DISEASES		
GLASSES / CONTACT LENSES	DENTURES / HEARING AIDS / ETC.	
FAMILY MEDICAL INFORMATION OF NOTE:		

MEDICAL INFORMATION # 2

DOCTORS

1. Name_____

   Address_____

   Telephone #_____ Specialization_____

   Treatment began_____ Patient ID #_____

   Treatment_____

   _____

   Medications prescribed / date_____

   _____

2. Name_____

   Address_____

   Telephone #_____ Specialization_____

   Treatment began_____ Patient ID #_____

   Treatment_____

   _____

   Medications prescribed / date_____

   _____

3. Name_____

   Address_____

   Telephone #_____ Specialization_____

   Treatment began_____ Patient ID #_____

   Treatment_____

   Medications prescribed / date_____

DENTISTS

1. Name_____

   Address_____

   Telephone #_____ Specialization_____

   Treatment began_____ Patient ID #_____

   Treatment_____

   Medications prescribed / date_____

2. Name_____

   Address_____

   Telephone #_____ Specialization_____

   Treatment began_____ Patient ID #_____

   Treatment_____

   Medications prescribed / date_____

3. Name_____

   Address_____

   Telephone #_____ Specialization_____

   Treatment began_____ Patient ID #_____

   Treatment_____

   Medications prescribed / date_____

IMMUNIZATION RECORD

Name_____

Birthdate _____

TYPE	DATE	DOSE	PHYSICIAN
Diphtheria Tetanus Pertussis			
Poliomyelitis			
Measles Mumps Rubella			
Smallpox			
Tuberculin Text			
Tetanus			
Pneumonia			
Other			

HOSPITALIZATION RECORD

Name_____

Birthdate _____

TYPE	DATE	TREATMENT	PHYSICIAN

TAKING CARE OF YOUR BODY

CHORES TO BE DONE	Daily	Twice Weekly	Weekly	Twice Monthly	Monthly	Twice Yearly	3 Times Yearly	Yearly
Apply make-up								
Apply perfume / after shave								
Apply deodorant / antiperspirant								
Bleach skin spots								
Bleach facial hair								
Breathe--deep and life giving	X							
Brush teeth. Floss. Use mouthwash								
Change clothes / underwear / socks								
Clean contact lenses / glasses								
Clean combs and brushes								
Clean dentures								
Cleanse / moisturize face								
Dental check up								
Drink--water, juices, good fluids	X							
Eat--lots of healthy foods	X							
Exercise / recreation								
Eye pack to reduce swelling								
Eye / vision examination								
Facial								
Hair: color								
Hair: condition								
Hair: curl, brush or blow dry								
Hair: cut								
Hair: permanent or straighten								
Hair: shampoo								
Hair removal from body								
Manicure								
Massage								
Medical / physical check up								

CHORES TO BE DONE	Daily	Twice Weekly	Weekly	Twice Monthly	Monthly	Twice Yearly	3 Times Yearly	Yearly
Medications for health challenges								
Meditate / Ponder / Reflect / Plan								
Mental health--stress free time / activities / hobbies								
Moisturize hands, elbows, feet, skin, lips, face								
Pedicure, foot massage								
Powder / spray / soak feet								
Replace toothbrush (3-6 months)								
Replace mascara or eye products (3-6 months)								
Replace makeup / lotions / personal & sanitary products as needed								
Replace medications								
Shave								
Shower / Bathe								
Sleep--get plenty	X							
Tweeze eyebrows								
Vitamins / Herbs								

HOUSEHOLD MAINTENANCE

When we were little, we believed that after we grew up we would hire a maid to clean our house. In fact, this dream is probably as common in childhood as the dream of marrying a handsome prince or a beautiful princess. To embellish the dream, most of us thought we would marry a wealthy person who would employ a housekeeper or butler or cook. We wouldn't even have to bother with interviewing the servants! Then how come so many of us end up doing our own household chores?

Little did we know that every time mother made us do our chores and we retorted, "When I grow up, I am going to have a maid to do all that work," Mom knew something we did not. There are not enough maids to go around. Mother kept this secret since she knew that reality would teach us about the maid shortage.

All those years you ignored learning how to get gum out of the wall-to-wall carpet have caught up with you and now--with no maid in sight, and mother retired--it is up to you to clean your house by yourself. You may even have a somewhat helpful spouse and assorted children who tell you, "This work is beneath my abilities. When I grow up I will be wealthy enough to hire a maid to do this work." In one fell swoop they have let you know that housework is an ordeal good enough for you but not for them, and if you were smarter, you would earn enough money to have somebody else show up once a week.

After years of struggling with this problem, I changed my style of housekeeping. This is one area of life that needs major subdividing. My free time for housekeeping does not come in hours. Minutes are my time frame for housecleaning. What can I get done in fifteen minutes when every square foot of space needs help? Easy. I subdivide this staggering job into compact tasks that do not make me feel overwhelmed.

The responsibility for cleaning and maintaining a house takes major organization. I devised a chart that subdivides this responsibility into small groups such as Soft Fabric Care or Lights and Windows. Then each section groups chores together under these subdivided categories. Some chores take fifteen minutes to complete and some are half day chores. The Household Maintenance List is large because there are so many chores to complete. Each line is a subdivided chore, small enough for you to schedule without feeling defeated.

You may either plan out your calendar for Household Maintenance as described in Section 1 or you may glance at the List and decide which tasks need to be done in your house. First decide which chores you want to complete within the next year.

There are two Basic Household Maintenance Lists with the same information but different formats.
- If you want to schedule your chores, keep reading the next paragraphs and complete **Household Maintenance List #1** on Page 72.
- If you do <u>not</u> want to schedule your chores and only want ideas about it takes to maintain a home, skip to **Household Maintenance—Regular Chores List # 2** on Page 78.

Instructions for Household Maintenance List #1—For people who want to plan their work

As you go through the list, determine which chores apply to you and your lifestyle. Fireplace cleaning will not be scheduled by someone who does not have a fireplace. Do not go too far down the list, because you have to fill in the section to the right on each line.

As you read down the chart, you get to choose how often you are going to do these chores. This is the part when your mother (or pretend maid) would cringe. They know you may choose to change your sheets every six months instead of once a week. Since you are an adult, you get to make the household chore, time table decision.

To the right of each line are eight columns. You decide if you want to do that chore daily, weekly, monthly or yearly. You can also choose twice weekly, twice monthly, twice yearly or three times a year. There are symbols to indicate your choice. Under (2xW) indicating two times a week, you might put a "3" or "4" to do something three or four times a week. Live it up. Be imaginative. Once again, use a pencil to fill this in and you can go back later and change your mind with your eraser. Nothing is mandated forever in this time scheduling.

(Sample of Household Maintenance List)

Chores To-Be-Done *MARK:(D=Daily)(W=Weekly)(2xW=Twice Week)(M=Monthly)* *(2xM=Twice month)(Y=Yearly)(2xY-Twice year)(3xY=Three year)*	D	W	2x W	M	2x M	Y	2x Y	3x Y

Go line by line. Decide to schedule the chore. Or decide to ignore the chore if you never want to bother with that task. If you select to schedule it, put an "X" under one of the time columns. Do not let filling in the list conquer you. Looking at all those tasks to be done may appear to be a mountain of work, but your mountain of housecleaning is being subdivided into mounds which are manageable.

Be realistic. You are not going to clean your washer and dryer every week even though you think it would be a great idea. Know your limitations and work within the time in your life available for household maintenance. Circumstances dictate the amount of time to be given each chore. For example, a mother of a newborn baby needs to scale back the time spent in this category.

After you have gone line by line through the List and assigned a symbol to each item (or crossed it off), you are ready to schedule the chores. This is taught in Section One.

Every housekeeper needs to pick-up odds and ends left around the house every day. You can plan to spend five or ten minutes on that chore daily.

Is your housecleaning style to clean the whole room at one time? You may like to enter a room and clean around the room in a circle, polishing and dusting as you go. Room by room house cleaners group chores together by location. If you prefer that method, combine the subdivided chores into groups of chores and accomplish them room by room.

To schedule the chores using my method, you need to copy twelve of the **Monthly To-Do Lists** and at least four of the **Weekly To-Do Lists**. Assign one month (January-December) to each of the **Monthly To-Do Lists**. Assign a date at the top of each of the **Weekly To-Do Lists**. On the website, www.listorganizer.com there are pre-dated **Weekly To-Do Lists** or you may copy them from this book for your personal use.

Next, the chores are scheduled on your **Weekly and Monthly To-Do Lists** or calendar depending on which method you've chosen. The chores you marked on the **Household Maintenance List # 1** as something you want to do "Monthly" "Yearly" or in between a month and year, will be scheduled on your **Monthly-To-Do Lists,** included in Chapter 4.. These chores are scheduled on a **Monthly To-Do List**, a page for January through December, but you can start using them in any month of the year

MONTHLY TO-DO LIST (Sample)

Fill in chores you want to accomplish this month
January, February, March, April, May, June, July, August, September, October, November, December *(Circle one for each month)*

☑	**HOUSEHOLD MAINTENANCE**	☑	**FINANCIAL**

Example: Your 12 pages may include some chores to be done once every month, such as wash the dog. List, "Wash the dog" on all 12 pages since it needs to be done every month.

You may have something that needs to be done every other month. List that chore on 6 of the monthly pages, skipping a month between.
Example: January, March, May, July, September, November

A chore to be done 4 times a year will be listed on 4 monthly pages with two months between.
Example: February, May, August, November

Twice yearly chores will be listed on two monthly pages with five months between.
Example: March, September
And a yearly chore will be listed only on one page.

The second List I use is a **Weekly To-Do List,** included in Chapter 4. The chores you want to do less than once a month go on your Weekly To-Do pages. Let me say again that I don't use a Daily To-Do List since I kept failing at getting things done and then I went into failure mode with a daily list giving me only 24 hours to finish everything.

WEEKLY TO-DO LIST (Sample)

	Fill in the chores you want to accomplish this week (Date)_____		
☑	**HOUSEHOLD MAINTENANCE**	☑	**FOOD**

The Weekly To-Do List is similar to a daily list except it gives me 168 hours to complete everything on the list. I like the possibility that I can get most of the things completed by the end of the week in my 168 hours of work time. Most people seem to know how to put together a short daily list and they are wonderful for short term goals, but many times they set you up for failure on your long term chores.

Now you can forget about when chores need to be done. They are planned and will be done in an orderly fashion. The logistics of keeping a house clean is easy since you can see at a glance what month the drapes will be cleaned and when to polish the silver.

An added advantage is you stop worrying about this information. Your mind is not bothered by the dirty shower curtain since it is scheduled for cleaning next month. All the mindless trivia concerning things you need to do is transferred from your mind to the planning calendar.

At this point:

Your Weekly-To-Do chores are scheduled on one, two, three or four **Weekly To-Do Lists**. And your Monthly-To-Do chores are scheduled on the twelve **Monthly-To-Do Lists**.

When convenient during each week, consult the **Weekly To-Do List** and complete the chores you have prioritized and needing to be done more than once a week or as critical. Complete as many of those tasks as you can. Then if you have extra time, look at the **Monthly-To-Do List** for this month and see if you have time to complete any of those chores.

When you cannot get chores done, remember to rotate forward and reschedule them another week or month. You are not failing when you cannot get everything done today. You are scheduling it to be done at a new time—next week or the next week or the next month.

Continue planning your life according to your schedule. This is a planning system to help you schedule your time. There are no instructions for how-to-do-it only when-to-do-it. Learn to Plan, Schedule and Do the Work. It makes life much simpler.

To recap: To the right of each line in the Household Maintenance List # 1 are eight columns. You decide if you want to do that chore daily, weekly, monthly or yearly. You may also choose twice weekly, twice monthly, twice yearly or three times a year. There are symbols to indicate your choice. Under (2xW) indicating two times a week, you might put a "3" or "4" to do something three or four times a week.

(Sample of Household Maintenance List)

Chores To-Be-Done	D	W	2x W	M	2x M	Y	2x Y	3x Y
MARK:(D=Daily)(W=Weekly)(2xW=Twice Week)(M=Monthly) *(2xM=Twice month)(Y=Yearly)(2xY-Twice year)(3xY=Three year)*								

Instructions for Household Maintenance List #2—For people who want a check off list of chores to be completed for a clean house.

. List # 2 is a sub-divided list of chores that are needed for household maintenance. The instructions to use this List are very simple. Look at List # 2, decide which chores need your attention and start to do the work when you have time. Keep working at completing all the items you've selected until your house is clean according to your standards. In a few days or weeks, refer to the List again and maintain your house by completing the chores again. Coordinate the routine chores on List # 2 with the **Deep Cleaning Lists** which have more detailed chores.

Household Maintenance Section Includes These Lists:

HOUSEHOLD MAINTENANCE LIST # 1

HOUSEHOLD MAINTENANCE—REGULAR CHORES #2

I FEEL LIKE DEEP CLEANING—SPRING CLEANING

DEEP CLEAN THE BATHROOMS

DEEP CLEAN THE BEDROOMS

DEEP CLEAN THE KITCHEN

REFILL LIST

REORGANIZE A STORAGE AREA

DEEP CLEAN THE GREAT OUTDOORS

TAKING CARE OF A GARDEN

TAKING CARE OF A PET

HOUSEHOLD MAINTENANCE LIST # 1

Chores To-Be-Done *MARK:(D=Daily)(W=Weekly)(2xW=Twice Week)(M=Monthly)* *(2xM=Twice month)(Y=Yearly)(2xY-Twice year)(3xY=Three year)*	D	W	2x W	M	2x M	Y	2x Y	3x Y
SOFT FABRIC ITEMS: Wash curtains								
Dry clean drapes								
Dust/wash window blinds								
Shake dust from curtains / dust top curtain rod								
Vacuum drapes								
SOFT FLOORS: Vacuum carpets								
Shampoo carpets								
Shake throw rugs								
Wash throw rugs								
Apply soil retardant to carpets								
BEDROOMS: Make beds								
Change/wash sheets								
Wash dust ruffles, bedspreads								
Wash blankets, comforters, quilts								
Wash mattress pad								
Turn mattress								
Vacuum mattress / bed frame								
BATH: Wash bath mats								
Wash shower curtain								
Wash bathroom towels	D							
KITCHEN: Wash kitchen towels								
Wash table cloth								
Wash place mats								
SOFT FURNITURE: Vacuum couch / chairs								
Shampoo upholstered furniture								
Turn cushions on couch / chairs								
Patch/ mend upholstered furniture								
Oil leather furniture								
Move couch/ chairs / beds to clean underneath								

Chores To-Be-Done *MARK:(D=Daily)(W=Weekly)(2xW=Twice Week)(M=Monthly)* *(2xM=Twice month)(Y=Yearly)(2xY-Twice year)(3xY=Three year)*	D	W	2x W	M	2x M	Y	2x Y	3x Y
FURNITURE: Dust furniture								
Polish/ wax furniture								
Refinish or patch wood								
Move wood furniture to clean underneath								
APPLIANCES: Dust top of refrigerator								
Clean refrigerator (shelves, gasket, crispers, door)								
Empty drip pan under refrigerator / freezer								
Vacuum coils on refrigerator / freezer								
Defrost freezer. Clean drip pan/ gasket.								
Clean oven								
Clean range top (drip pans, knobs, grease holder)								
Replace drip pans								
Clean around pilot light / air vents on gas range								
Clean range hood / exhaust filter								
Clean microwave								
Clean dishwasher (spray arm, filter trap)								
Clean coffeepot								
Clean electric can opener / knife sharpener								
Clean toaster / toaster oven (crumbs)								
Clean trash compactor								
Clean blender / food processor/ mixer								
Clean/ wax exterior of kitchen appliances								
Clean television screens								
Clean telephones								
Clean clothes washer and dryer								
Change or empty vacuum / clean bag								
Clean vacuum cleaner roller								
HARD CARE SURFACE: Sweep floors								
Mop floors								
Wax floors								
Strip old wax off floors								

Chores To-Be-Done *MARK:(D=Daily)(W=Weekly)(2xW=Twice Week)(M=Monthly)* *(2xM=Twice month)(Y=Yearly)(2xY-Twice year)(3xY=Three year)*	D	W	2x W	M	2x M	Y	2x Y	3x Y
Remove black marks from floors								
Fix squeaks in floors								
Sand / refinish wood floors								
Replace broken ceramic tiles								
Clean spider webs								
Dust walls / spot wash them								
Wash walls								
Paint walls								
Strip wallpaper / re-wallpaper								
Dust doors / ledges								
Wash doors								
Lubricate door hinges / locks								
Dust baseboards / molding								
Clean cupboard doors and handles								
Clean bathroom vanity								
Clean washbasins / sinks								
Clean toilets								
Clean showers / bathtubs								
Clean mildew off tiles								
Clean tile grout								
Clean toilet paper / towel holders								
Clean soap dishes								
Caulk tubs/ sinks / back splashes								
Clean glass shower door								
Polish cupboard wood								
Wipe countertops								
Polish countertops								
Sand/ oil cutting boards / butcher blocks								
LIGHTS & WINDOWS: Dust lamp shades								
Clean chandelier and light covers								
Wipe light switches / electric outlets								

LISTS FOR MUDDLE MANAGEMENT

Chores To-Be-Done *MARK:(D=Daily)(W=Weekly)(2xW=Twice Week)(M=Monthly)* *(2xM=Twice month)(Y=Yearly)(2xY-Twice year)(3xY=Three year)*	D	W	2x W	M	2x M	Y	2x Y	3x Y
Replace burned out light bulbs								
Wash windows inside								
Wash windows outside								
Change storm windows								
Change door / window screens								
Clean sliding glass door								
Clean door / window slide tracks--lubricate								
Clean window sills								
Polish mirrors								
DECORATIONS: Polish silver								
Polish brass/ copper/ pewter								
Dust figurines								
Dust picture frames								
Clean glass fronts of pictures								
Dust books / bookshelves								
Straighten books / magazines / table decorations								
Discard magazines								
Clean bottles, miscellaneous items on dressers								
Clean ashtrays								
CUPBOARDS / DRAWERS: Wash shelf paper								
Replace shelf paper								
Organize drawers (One a week or month)								
Straighten cupboards								
Clean out medicine cabinets								
PLUMBING: Flush drains								
Clean faucet heads								
Change automatic toilet bowl cleaner								
Drain hot water heater / clean								
Clean septic tank / add activator								
Change water purification filters								

Chores To-Be-Done *MARK:(D=Daily)(W=Weekly)(2xW=Twice Week)(M=Monthly)* *(2xM=Twice month)(Y=Yearly)(2xY-Twice year)(3xY=Three year)*	D	W	2x W	M	2x M	Y	2x Y	3x Y
Setup sprinkler system for season								
Drain sprinkler system								
HEATING: Dust or vacuum radiator								
Bleed radiator								
Vacuum heat registers								
Wash heat registers								
Change blower (furnace) filter								
Change air-conditioner filter								
Service furnace / lubricate								
Straighten blade fins on convectors								
Lubricate electric heaters								
Clean humidifier / or de-humidifier								
Clean/ service ceiling fans								
Have coal/ fuel oil delivered								
Remove fireplace ashes (after they cool)								
Clean chimney								
Clean fireplace glass and tools								
Clean fireplace bricks								
Replace woodpile wood								
Clean wood burning stove								
OUTDOORS: Clean downspouts								
Clean gutters								
Replace faulty roof parts								
Straighten TV antenna								
Paint exterior								
Clean driveway / garage concrete								
Remove junk / garden clippings								
Replace/ fix broken play equipment								
Clean mailbox								
Move outdoor furniture from storage								
Move outdoor furniture to storage								

Chores To-Be-Done *MARK:(D=Daily)(W=Weekly)(2xW=Twice Week)(M=Monthly)* *(2xM=Twice month)(Y=Yearly)(2xY-Twice year)(3xY=Three year)*	D	W	2x W	M	2x M	Y	2x Y	3x Y
Clean barbecue grill								
Straighten garage								
Clean window wells								
Do insect / pest check								
Clean patio								
Rinse outside walls / siding								
Repairs nails in siding								
Replace caulk on siding								
MISCELLANEOUS: Sharpen knives								
Organize loose keys / padlocks								
Record combination numbers for combination locks								
Empty trash								
Clean trash pails / waste baskets								
Change bags in waste baskets								
Wash brooms and mops								
Change smoke detector batteries								
Check fire extinguishers								

HOUSEHOLD MAINTENANCE— REGULAR CHORES # 2

Soft Fabric Items	Kitchen	Appliances
Wash curtains	Wash kitchen towels	Dust top of refrigerator
Dry clean drapes	Wash table cloth / place mats	Clean refrigerator (shelves /gasket/door)
Dust / wash window blinds	Wash pot holders	Empty drip pan under refrigerator /freezer
Vacuum drapes and curtains	Wipe countertops / polish	Empty drip pan under ice dispenser
Dust top of curtain rods	Empty dishwasher / put away dishes	Vacuum coils on refrigerator / freezer
Soft Flooring	Clean cabinet doors and handles	Defrost freezer. Clean drip pan /gasket
Vacuum carpets	Clean tile and walls	Clean oven
Shampoo carpets	Sand / oil cutting boards	Clean range top and knobs
Shake throw rugs	Sharpen knives	Clean or replace drip pans
Wash throw rugs	Straighten cupboards / drawers	Clean range hood / exhaust filter
Apply soil retardant to carpets	Empty trash throughout house	Clean microwave
Hard Flooring	Clean kitchen sink	Clean dishwasher inside and outside
Sweep or dust floors	**Lights**	Clean coffeepot
Mop floors	Dust lamp shades	Clean electric can opener / knife sharpener
Wax floors (Strip off old wax)	Clean chandelier and light covers	Clean toaster / toaster oven of crumbs
Remove black marks from floors	Wipe light switches / electric outlets	Clean trash compactor
Fix squeaks in floors	Replace burned out light bulbs	Clean blender / food processor / mixer
Sand / refinish wood floors	**Furniture Fabrics**	Clean exterior of kitchen appliances
Bedrooms Fabrics	Vacuum couch / chairs	Clean clothes washer and dryer (lint)
Make beds	Shampoo upholstered furniture	Change or empty vacuum cleaner bag
Change / wash sheets	Turn cushions on couch / chairs	Clean vacuum cleaner roller
Wash dust ruffles, bedspreads	Dry clean slipcovers	**Electronics**
Wash blankets, comforters, quilts	Clean / oil leather furniture	Dust and clean television screens
Wash mattress pad	Move furniture to clean underneath	Clean telephones / Reset Caller ID boxes
Turn mattress	**Furniture Hard Surface**	Clean computer surfaces and screen
Vacuum mattress / bed frame	Dust, remove cobwebs	Clean amplifiers/ speakers / components
	Polish / wax	
	Refinish or patch wood	

Bathroom	Windows	Decorations
Wash bath mats	Wash windows inside	Polish silver / brass / copper / pewter
Wash shower curtain or replace	Wash windows outside	Dust figurines / ceramics
Wash bathroom towels	Change storm windows	Dust picture frames / glass fronts
Clean bathroom vanity	Change door / window screens	Dust books / bookshelves
Clean sinks / tubs / shower stalls	Clean door and window slide tracks / lubricate or replace rollers	Discard magazines / papers
Clean toilets inside and out	Clean window sills and ledges	Straighten books / magazines/ table decorations
Clean mildew off tile and grout	Polish mirrors	Clean dresser bottles & decorations
Refill toilet paper / paper cups / soap dispensers / air freshener		Clean ashtrays
Clean soap dishes		Water and dust plants
Clean and shine mirrors		Wind clocks
Straighten shelves and drawers		Straighten CDs, Music
Clean cupboard doors and handles		
Change toilet bowl cleaner		

About once a year we get the urge to really clean the house. We used to call this spring cleaning, but it can be done anytime. There are some heavy duty cleaning jobs that take more muscle and time. This list has a few of those chores listed for those Saturdays when you just feel like cleaning.

I FEEL LIKE DEEP CLEANING—SPRING CLEANING

Cupboard and Drawers	Outdoors
• Wash or replace shelf paper	• Clean downspouts
• Organize drawers (one a week is good)	• Clean roof gutters
• Straighten cupboards	• Replace faulty roof parts
• Clean out medicine cabinets	• Paint exterior
	• Clean driveway and garage floor concrete
Plumbing	• Remove junk / garden clippings
• Flush drains	• Replace / fix broken play equipment
• Clean faucet heads and handles	• Clean or repaint mailbox
• Drain hot water heater / Clean	• Move outdoor furniture from storage / Paint
• Clean septic tank / add activator	• Store outdoor furniture for winter
• Change water purification filters	• Clean barbecue grill
• Setup sprinkler system for season (or drain)	• Straighten garage
	• Clean trash out of window wells
Heating	• Do insect / pest check
• Dust or vacuum radiator	• Clean patio
• Bleed radiator	• Rinse outside walls / siding
• Vacuum and wash heat registers	• Repair nails in siding
• Have heating system cleaned	• Repair caulk on siding
• Change furnace (blower) filter	• Wash windows and screens
• Change air conditioner filter	
• Service furnace / lubricate	

•	Miscellaneous
• Straighten blade fins on convectors	• Organize loose keys / padlocks
• Lubricate electric heaters	• Wash out trash pails / waste baskets
• Clean humidifier / or de-humidifier	• Wash brooms and mops
• Clean / service ceiling fans	• Change smoke detector batteries--twice a year
• Remove fireplace ashes (after they cool)	• Check fire extinguishers
• Have chimney/wood burning stove cleaned	• Take down the outdoor Christmas lights.
• Purchase firewood or coal	• Polish staircase rails
• Clean gas burners in fireplace	• Service clocks
• Clean fireplace bricks and glass	• Service vacuum (bag, roller, belts)
• Clean wood burning stove	• Service appliances

DEEP CLEAN THE BATHROOMS

To clean my bathrooms I need to:	Bathroom #1	Bathroom #2	Bathroom #3
Buy good cleansers and brushes for this job			
Clean the bathtubs, grout and faucets			
Clean the sinks, countertops and faucets			
Clean the toilets, scrub inside basin, disinfect outside of toilet			
Clean the shower stalls, glass doors, faucets			
Wash or replace shower curtains, replace broken hooks			
Clean shower curtain rods			
Wash or replace bath mats and scatter rugs			
Wash or replace towels and washcloths			
Wash window curtains or dust window blinds			
Wash windows and frames			
Dust away cobwebs			
Polish mirrors			
Sweep and mop floors			
Empty wastebaskets, wash wastebaskets			
Clean tile in tubs, showers, backsplashes			
Clean and wash clothes hampers			
Clean walls, doors, doorknobs			
Clean light switches and electrical outlet switches			
Fill soap and lotion dispensers			
Replace toilet scrub brush			
Throw out old lotions, shampoos, soaps, shaving goods, etc.			
Throw out old cosmetics, makeup, lipstick, mascara, etc.			
Wash makeup brushes, hair brushes, combs and curlers			
Throw out old heating pads, massagers, blow dryers, curling irons			
Throw out unnecessary junk--all of it			
Rethink your space requirements--buy organizers, shelves, drawers, baskets, hooks, or hanging organizers and redo your bathroom storage space on shelves and under the sink			

To clean my bathrooms I need to:	Bathroom #1	Bathroom #2	Bathroom #3
Scrub shelves in medicine cabinet			
Discard old medications and prescriptions			
Move medications to a secure place			
Update your First Aid Kit			
Change razor blades in shavers, clean electric shavers			
Clean weigh-in scales			
Replace shelf paper on shelves			
Paint--if walls need it and you're ambitious			
Extras:			

DEEP CLEAN THE BEDROOMS

To clean my bedrooms I need to:	Bedroom #1	Bedroom #2	Bedroom #3
Remove mattress & box springs from bed, Flip mattress			
Dust bed frames while mattress is removed			
Remove clutter & vacuum or dust floor under bed			
Remove dust ruffle, clean, replace			
Clean bedspreads, comforters, sheets, shams, pillowcases			
Dust bed headboard and footboard			
Clean light fixtures, replace light bulbs			
Clean light switches, electrical outlets, television outlets			
Vacuum or shampoo carpet			
Replace or clean throw rugs			
Vacuum or clean molding strips (Vacuum carpet close to molding)			
Dust wood and tile floors. Mop			
Polish mirrors. Dust top of mirrors			
Clean windows & window sills			
Clean window coverings--draperies, blinds, shutters, shades			
Dust and clean curtain rods and fixtures			
Clean door handles. Dust top of doors and picture frames			
Rearrange pictures on walls			
Dust ceiling & corners of walls			
Wash or dust walls			
Remove clutter from top of dressers, tables			
Dust and polish tables/ dressers / armoires/ entertainment centers			
Remove dresser drawers and dust underneath drawers			
Dust figurines, decorations			
Replace candles and air fresheners			
Dust and repair electronic equipment--Televisions, VCRs, DVD players, Alarm clocks, CD players, Telephones, Answering machine			
Rearrange CDs, Videotapes, DVDs, Cassettes			
Clear out Books, Magazines, Files & Stacks of papers			

To clean my bedrooms I need to:	Bedroom #1	Bedroom #2	Bedroom #3
Buy better drawer organizers--or make them			
Straighten sock drawers (Match or throw out)			
Straighten pantyhose (Throw out, arrange by color, size)			
Straighten lingerie, underwear drawer			
Straighten or arrange accessories:			
Scarves			
Gloves			
Hats			
Purses, wallets			
Straighten jewelry (Watches, Bracelets, Necklaces, Rings, Etc.)			
Dust jewelry boxes			
Straighten hair accessories:			
Brushes & combs (Clean)			
Bobby pins, hairpins, hair clips			
Headbands, hair styling accessories			
Blow dryers, Curling irons, Electric rollers, Curlers			
Hairnets, turbans & all the rest			
Replace makeup organizers			
Straighten & discard makeup			
Foundation			
Mascara (Every 3-4 months)			
Eye shadows, applicators, eye pencils, eye liners			
Blush and brushes			
Lipsticks, lip liners, lip brushes, lip balms			
Straighten & repair tweezers, scissors			
Replace cotton balls, makeup applicators, tissues, cotton swabs			
Straighten & discard nail products Nail polish, base & topcoats, strengtheners Cuticle remover Emery boards, nail scissors, buffers Pedicure materials, pumice stone			
Rearrange clothes in dresser drawers (sweaters, swimsuits, etc.)			

Clean out other drawers in dressers and armoires:			
Papers, charge card slips, bank statements, address books			
Batteries (test for charge)			
Money, coins			
Keys, key holders			
Office supplies			
Use the Clothes List to clean out your closet			
Use the Bathroom List to clean your bathroom			

Add any extras that are unique to your situation. Then get ready for a restful night's sleep in an organized, good-smelling, dust free bedroom.

DEEP CLEAN THE KITCHEN

On the list below, mark each column next to each task. Mark #1 column, if you know this has to be done, #2 column, think you should do this, #3 column, know you won't bother because it doesn't apply or you don't care. My tip: Try those new disposable dust, mop and disinfectant sheets. They seem to make things cleaner.

To clean my kitchen I need to:	#1 Priority	Maybe I'll Do It	Forget About It
Buy good cleansers, brushes, mops, brooms for this job			
Purchase new containers / organizers / turntables / shelves			
Purchase new shelf paper			
Cabinets and drawer fronts-- Clean and polish. Remove scratches, Fix hinges, cracks, etc.			
Range and oven--Clean the inside, Clean or replace reflector pans. Clean exterior, buttons, door. Clean the range hood. Clean hood's filter.			
Refrigerator--Remove contents and throw away expired foods. Wash shelves, meat bin, and vegetable crisper. Replace burned out light bulbs. Vacuum condenser coils. Remove magnets, etc. from exterior. Clean exterior--include top. Clean gasket. Replace the food grouping like items together.			
Freezer--Defrost if necessary. Remove food and throw away expired foods. Clean interior. Clean drip pan and tubes. Clean exterior. Clean gasket. Replace the food grouping like items.			
Dishwasher--Clean exterior. Clean holes in rotating arms. Clean inside. Add rinse additive.			
Microwave--Scrub inside to remove splatters and food. Clean inside trays. Clean exterior.			
Trash compactor--Clean exterior. Change bag. Clean inside.			
Small appliances--Check cords for wear on all small appliances. Throw out all gadget appliances you no longer use.			
Blender/ Food Processor / Mixer / Juicer--Clean exterior. Wipe off blades or attachments. Wash bowls or glass containers.			
Toaster--Empty crumb tray. Polish exterior			
Electric can opener--Remove blade and clean. Clean exterior			
Coffee maker--Clean inside and out			
Waffle maker--Clean waffle plates. Polish exterior			
Water filtration system--Change filter. Clean exterior			
Any specialized small appliances--Clean inside and outside			
Paint or clean walls, backsplashes and ceiling			

To clean my kitchen I need to:	#1 Priority	Maybe I'll Do It	Forget About It
Wash or clean blinds, shutters, curtains			
Wash windows, screens,			
Clean baseboards, molding.			
Clean light and electric switches.			
Doors--Polish and oil hinges. Sliding door--Clean runner and glass. Clean handles.			
Clean telephones			
Dust furniture. Dust away cobwebs.			
Clean table and chairs, bar stools.			
Clean light fixtures			
Sweep, mop, wax floors.			
Clean or bleach sink. Clean around faucets.			
Deodorize garbage disposal. (Use lemon rind or vinegar)			
Check under sink and faucet for leaks. Call plumber for leaks and clogs.			
Replace old cleansers, sponges, scrubbers, mops, brooms, etc.			
Clean or replace dish drainer.			
Clean bread box.			
Wash tablecloths, place mats, dishcloths, dish rags, pot holders, etc.			
Scrub wastebaskets, inside and out.			
Prune and water plants			
Sharpen knives and scissors			
Clear out message center or bulletin boards. Clean up mail, papers, etc.			
Clear out cookbooks, recipes, index cards. Organize in books or containers.			
Clean off countertop and polish			
Refill the items on the Refill Home Products List:			
Cupboards—Reorganize, rethink, redo. Throw out old dishes, glasses.			

REFILL HOME PRODUCTS

We buy lots of large sizes of products and transfer them into smaller containers. Now refill or replace all of these items at once and forget about these little chores. The products listed are items that you would not refill everyday. Don't forget to add water to concentrated products and put them into spray bottles or containers.

Clean and Refill / replace containers for these products: Non-Food containers	Clean and Refill containers for these products: Food containers
Air freshener scents	Flour & sugar canisters
Batteries in flashlights, toys, smoke detectors, etc.	Honey bottles
Cleaner, all purpose spray or cleanser	Jelly jars
Cotton balls & swabs & makeup pads	Ketchup and mustard containers
Dishwashing detergent & rinse additive	Margarine or butter containers
Glass cleaner	Mayonnaise containers
Hair spray, non-aerosol	Oil and vinegar cruet
Mouthwash	Powdered sugar or cinnamon sugar
Napkins	Rice or noodles or spaghetti
Pan scrubber	Salt and pepper shakers
Paper towels	Tea and coffee plus filters
Razor blades in razors	Vitamins & medications
Shampoo / conditioner / hair products	Extras: In refrigerator, throw out items with expired dates
Soap, liquid or bar	
Sponge	
Tissues	
Toilet paper	
Toothpaste	
Travel size bottles for vacation	

REORGANIZE A STORAGE AREA

Choose the storage area in your home that needs the most help. It might be small like a closet or big like the garage. What storage area would you love to have clean? That's the one you need to clean.

Before you start to clean out, visualize the look of the new space. This is especially important if you are doing a large area like a garage.

- Assign areas (Everything gets grouped with matching items):
    - Examples: For a garage: Tools, Athletic equipment, Auto equipment, Trash, Pets, Lawn and Garden
    - For an indoor closet: Shoes, Clothes, Towels, Linens, Cameras, Games
    - For a storage room: Food, Cleaning & sanitary supplies, Gift wrap, Photographs and Slides, Christmas-Easter-Halloween supplies, Craft supplies.
- Begin the process of moving out, cleaning out and rearranging.
    - Put all items into five boxes or bags or areas
        - Keep and return to new space
        - Keep and clean before putting away
        - Throw into trash
        - Give away to thrift store or charity
        - Sell at garage sale / Flea market

For those of you who have trouble deciding what to do I'll add

- Put aside item and have someone help you decide where it goes.

- Wash or clean the items you identified as needing repair and return them to their new space.
- Dispose of the trash
- Take items to thrift stores
- Mark items for a garage sale (Before you choose this, are you really going to have a garage sale?)
- Put away the treasures that remain.

DEEP CLEAN THE GREAT OUTDOORS

There comes a time in the year when we turn our thoughts to the patio, garden and outside of the house. Suddenly our work load increases with the addition of new outdoor chores. The variety of outdoor chores depends on you and the size of the plot of earth that you tend. So only chose the chores you need to do and disregard the rest. If you live in the southern hemisphere, change the months to fit your summer. These chores are not in order of completion.

To clean outdoors I need to:	May	June	July	August	September
Start bulbs and seeds indoors.					
Bring out hoses and sprinklers. Repair.					
Sweep and wash the patio					
Sweep and wash sidewalks, driveway, etc.					
Clean up leaves and trash in yard					
Bring out patio furniture. Paint or condition wood & metal.					
Clean cushions for furniture. Or replace.					
Clean patio umbrellas. Or replace.					
Clean awnings. Mend or replace.					
Clean out roof gutters. Repair.					
Repair roof and fireplace. Have chimney cleaned.					
Paint exterior and trim of house.					
Clean and treat deck wood.					
Turn on outdoor watering/sprinkler system.					
Fill, repair, maintain the outdoor pool or waterfall or misters					
Fertilize / weed lawn. Reseed bare spots in lawn.					
Aerate or rake lawn. Water lawn areas.					
Pooper-scoop lawn from pet messes.					
Mow and trim lawn areas.					
Trim bushes and trees of dead limbs and branches.					
Prune rose / flowering bushes.					
Fertilize bushes and trees.					
Weed gardens for planting.					
Haul away dead weeds, clippings, branches, etc.					
Plow / rototill garden areas. Prepare soil.					
Buy seeds, bedding plants, trees, etc.					
Plant containers and window boxes.					
Plant gardens according to your Garden Design.					

To clean outdoors I need to:	May	June	July	August	September
Fertilize and water gardens. Use Garden List to schedule.					
Repair fences/ gates / trellis. Paint if necessary.					
Maintain and repair air conditioners / fans / outdoor heater.					
Maintain and repair outdoor grill / cooker.					
Clean / repair outdoor games, trampoline, play sets.					
Repair patio, stepping stones, bricks, flagstone, etc.					
Spray weeds in lawn, rocks, gardens, etc.					
Spray for insect and disease control.					
Dig out and pull weeds.					
Maintain and repair garden tools and implements.					
Maintain and repair lawn mower / weed cutter / trimmer.					
Maintain and repair hot tub.					
Put stakes in garden & new trees					
Take off stakes from last year's trees					
Prepare hangers for hanging floral pots					
Trim hedges and borders.					
Divide and move plants/ bushes/ trees.					
Repair bird feeders. Replenish with food.					
Repair /rearrange compost area.					
Have an outdoor party.					
Sit outdoors and relax.					
Record plant history on Garden Maintenance List					

Gardeners are natural planners. They visualize in their minds how dirt and rocks will look with just a little help from them. Each type of plan takes tender care. Early blooming bulbs need a different plan than late blooming vegetables. Print out a copy of a garden plan for each type of plant or for each garden. Fill in the blanks and this planner will help you plan when to prune that rose bush. Cross off what you do not want. You may transfer this to a master planning calendar.

TAKING CARE OF A GARDEN

CHORES TO BE DONE	Daily	Twice Weekly	Weekly	Twice Monthly	Monthly	Twice Yearly	3 Times Yearly	Yearly
Pre-planning Plan or design garden. Draw blueprint. Type of garden or plant outlined on this page (Circle one) BULBS; FLOWER GARDEN; FRUITS; LAWNS; PLANTS (Annual, Perennial); SHRUBS, TREES, VEGETABLE GARDEN								
Purchase: Seeds, plants, trees Projected price:								
Soil preparation, till								
Plant, sow, reseed								
Mulch								
Water								
Feed, fertilize								
Spray								
Prune, thin								
Weed								
Mow								
Rake								
Dig/ divide								

CHORES TO BE DONE	Daily	Twice Weekly	Weekly	Twice Monthly	Monthly	Twice Yearly	3 Times Yearly	Yearly
Harvest								
Repair fences, trellises, etc.								
Extras:								

Keep track of what you've planted, what store sold it to you, how long it took for it to grow or germinate, if it did well in the shade or sun, or other items to help you maintain your garden year after year. You may modify this for trees and shrubs.

Name of plant / Variety:	**Date planted:**
Description of plant / tree / shrub	**Best in**: Shade; Sun; Semi-shade
Purchased from:	**Price:**
Notes:	**Spray or Insect Control Product:**
Harvest:	
Performance:	

Maintaining a garden (Record the maintenance on this plant / tree / shrub) Record when you feed, move, mulch, prune, spray, etc. each plant

Remember when Mom said, "Do you know how much work it is to take care of a dog?" Here's a list to help you remember that owning an animal is a big responsibility. Some animals are easier to take care of than others, but they all take work. Next to each chore, mark how often it needs to be done. Scratch through the chores you never do and ignore those. This gives you an idea of the time commitment for your pets. If you really want to be organized, transfer these commitments to a place on your planner or To-Do List.

TAKING CARE OF A PET

CHORES TO BE DONE	Daily	Twice Weekly	Weekly	Twice Monthly	Monthly	Twice Yearly	3 Times Yearly	Yearly
Bathe pet								
Brush and comb								
Clean house or cage								
Exercise, take for a walk								
Feed, fresh water								
Flea collar, change								
Groomed by professional								
License renewed								
Litter box changed / scooped								
Medication								
Nails clipped								
Teeth brushed								
Toys replaced or cleaned								
Vaccinations and boosters								
Veterinarian exam								
Don't forget playtime with your pet								
Extras:								

FISH:								
Check water temperature								
Change filters								
Add chemicals (waste eliminator, water neutralizers)								
Check air pump tubes								
Clean fish tank								
Clean accessories (plants and ornaments)								
Change water								

Take these items on a trip with your pet	
Bed / Bedding / Blanket	
Bottle with water for refilling water bowl	
Bowl for water	
Brush	
Carrying case / Kennel	
Dishes	
Food / Treats	
Identification tag	
Leash	
Pooper scooper	
Sedative	
Toys / Catnip	
Veterinarian records	

Books / CDs / DVDs Section Includes These Lists:

REORGANIZE BOOKS / VIDEOS / CDS

BOOKS TO READ / MOVIES TO SEE

RESEARCH PLANNER

LIBRARY or BORROWED BOOKS

REORGANIZE BOOKS / VIDEOS / CDS

Make those bookshelves look orderly, throw out old magazines and collect the videos that have strayed from their boxes with these instructions.. Organize your collections of music, books and movies.

Build or buy bookshelves to hold the books you want to display. (Modify this for your music and movie collections.)

- Assign areas to the books. Organize them by author or by subjects (examples: children's, cookbooks, business, reference, etc.) For music, organize by artist. For movies, organize by type or alphabetize.
- Begin the process of moving out, cleaning out and rearranging.
  - Put all items into five boxes or bags or areas. The areas are:
    - Keep and return to new space
    - Keep and clean before putting away
    - Throw into trash
    - Give away to thrift store or charity
    - Sell at garage sale / flea market

For those of you who have trouble deciding what to do I'll add

- Put aside item and have someone help you decide where it goes.

- Wash or clean the items you identified as needing repair and return them to their new space.

- Dispose of the trash
- Take items to thrift stores
- Mark items for a garage sale (Before you choose this, are you really going to have a garage sale?)
- Put away the treasures that remain
- Repeat this process for
  - Compact Discs
  - Magazines
  - Video Tapes
  - DVDs
  - Cassette tapes
  - Phonograph records
  - Sheet music and Music books
  - Any other entertainment-type collections

BOOKS TO READ / MOVIES TO SEE

List Titles of Books or Movies you want to read or see during the next 12 months

☑	TITLE	AUTHOR	Buy (Cost)	Rent / Borrow	Book/Movie

RESEARCH PLANNER

Main Topic	Title, Author or Library Call Number for Books/ Videos/ Etc.
Sub-Topic	Title, Author or Library Call Number for Books/ Videos/ Etc.
Sub-Topic	Title, Author or Library Call Number for Books/ Videos/ Etc.
Sub-Topic	Title, Author or Library Call Number for Books/ Videos/ Etc.

Take this list to the Library or Research Center with you. Keep track of the sources for your research project.

LIBRARY or BORROWED BOOKS

☑	TITLE	AUTHOR	Due Date	Renew Due Date	Return To

Cardholder's Name _____ This chart keeps track of your Library Books.
When you check out books from the library, fill in this chart. Column 2 is Title of Book. Column 3 is Author of Book. Column 4 is Date the book is due back to the library (Note the due date on your planning calendar or To-Do List.) Column 5 is the new due date if you renew the book or movie. Column 6 is the owner of the book (Library or individual.) Mark off column 1 when the book or video is returned.

HOUSEHOLD SET UP

In the olden days, women started preparing their hope chest when they were small children. Linens were embroidered; pottery was crafted; quilts were patched together. And this bundle of household goods was kept as a dowry for the lady when the marriage proposal arrived on bended knee. The husband-to-be might have brought along a horse and a strong back. Furniture was added as money permitted.

After the war years, merchandise for marriage chests was sold, door to door, by clever salesmen who would let the prospective bride purchase her china, silverware, or pots and pans on a "buy now--pay a little a month" plan.

The age of affluence brought a new attitude--"My Mom and Dad's friends will give me everything I need when I get married." Or, "When I go to college, Mom will take me to the discount store and we will buy whatever I need."

Approaches to furnishing a house may change, but the basic necessities stay the same. Oh, we may add food processors to the list, but sheets and pillowcases remain steady on the "I'm on my own now, what should I buy" list.

The Household Set Up chapter is a group of lists, indexing hundreds of items that are needed in a household. A college student may want to use the lists as a quick overview of what might be needed later when they are more settled. They may need to purchase very little to live in the small dormitory room and should use the **First Move Away From Home List**. A recently graduated high school student who is moving away from home will need to purchase items for a basic kitchen, clothing care, and linens for the bedroom and bath. A person, who really did get the house furnished at marriage time, may find it is now divorce time and they need a little help in determining what is needed to rearrange their new house needs. The settled homeowner may use the lists as wish lists for things they would like to buy someday.

As you go through the lists you get to choose what you want to buy right now because you have the money and the space and need it immediately. Or your budget and space allowance won't let you purchase all your desired whims this week so you're going to have to postpone buying some coveted wares. At Christmas or birthday time, see if there is something on the list that would be a nice gift to you.

If you get a handsome raise, you can refer to the list and then you can actually blow your money on something you need. Also, in retrospect, you may find you didn't want it all that badly.

Don't put off buying these essential items until they are needed. When you are dripping blood on the floor, it is too late to run out and buy a bandage. At 3 a.m. when the coughing fit starts, you need that cough suppressant or lozenge now. And a faulty digestive system waits for no shopping trip. It demands attention.

Household Set Up Section Includes These Lists:

STOCK THOSE SHELVES

CLEANING SUPPLIES

GETTING STARTED IN A KITCHEN

HOME MEDICAL SUPPLIES

SEWING KIT

TOOL KIT

FURNITURE AND MISCELLANEOUS

HOME EMERGENCY KIT

FIRST MOVE AWAY FROM HOME

The List for setting up a Laundry Room is with the Clothes Section

STOCK THOSE SHELVES

☐ Baking powder	☐ Mayonnaise	☐ Vanilla
☐ Baking soda	☐ Milk	☐ Vinegar
☐ Beans	☐ Mustard	☐ Worcestershire
☐ Bouillon cubes	☐ Oil (Canola, Olive, Vegetable)	☐ **Extras for the House**
☐ Bread	☐ Pasta	☐ Baby food & formula
☐ Butter or Margarine	☐ Pepper	☐ Batteries
☐ Cereal	☐ Rice	☐ Facial tissue
☐ Cheese	☐ Salt	☐ Film
☐ Cocoa	☐ Sauces (liquid and powdered)	☐ Light bulbs
☐ Coffee	☐ Shortening	☐ Napkins
☐ Cooking spray	☐ Spices	☐ Pet food
☐ Corn starch	☐ Soup	☐ Plastic bags and wraps
☐ Drink mixes	☐ Sugar, brown	☐ Toilet tissue
☐ Eggs	☐ Sugar, granulated	
☐ Flour	☐ Sugar, powdered	
☐ Herbs	☐ Syrup	
☐ Honey	☐ Tea	
☐ Ketchup	☐	
☐	☐	
☐	☐	

CLEANING SUPPLIES

What you need to maintain the household Pick and Choose and what is best for your needs	
➡ Bags for trash	➡ Razor blade scrapper
➡ Baking soda	➡ Silver and metal polish
➡ Bathroom cleaner	➡ Sponges
➡ Bleach	➡ Squeegee
➡ Broom	➡ Toilet plunger
➡ Brushes, (scrub, tile, etc.)	➡ Toothbrush (for small places)
➡ Bucket	➡ Vacuum cleaner
➡ Cloths for cleaning (rags)	➡ Vinegar
➡ Dish wash soap or detergent	➡ Wastebaskets
➡ Dust cloths or dust wands	➡ Wood cleaner and dusters
➡ Extension cords	➡ Extras:
➡ Floor cleanser	➡
➡ Glass cleanser	➡
➡ Gloves, latex	➡
➡ Kitchen cleaners, disinfectants	➡
➡ Mop	➡
➡ Oven cleaner	➡
➡ Powdered cleanser	➡

GETTING STARTED IN A KITCHEN

Knives: Bread Knife	**Utensils, Etc..** Can opener
Carving knife and fork	Colander
Chef's knife	Cutting board
Paring knives (more than one)	Forks, long handles
Sharpener	Funnel
Steak knives	Grater
Baking: Bread or loaf pan	Measuring cups and spoons
Cake pan (2) round 9 inch or 1 rectangular cake pan	Mixer
Cookie sheets (2)	Mixing bowls
Muffin tin	Pancake turner
Pie plate (2) round 9 inch	Peeler
Pizza pan or stone	Scraper
Rolling pin	Spatula
Pots and Pans: Baking dishes (3 sizes)	Spoons, wooden or metal long handles
Coffeepot	Tongs
Fry pans (2 sizes)	Whisks
Lids for dishes and pans	**Cleanup**: (See Cleaning Supplies)
Roasting pan	Dish drainer
Saucepans (3 sizes)	Dish towels and dish cloths
Tea Kettle	Scrubber and scraper
Dishes: Bowls (cereal or soup)	
Canisters	**Extras:**
Cups and plates	
Flatware	
Glasses, drinking	
Mugs	
Plates (dessert, dinner, salad)	
Salt and pepper shakers	

HOME MEDICAL SUPPLIES

LIST OF FIRST AID SUPPLIES	BATHROOM # 1	BATHROOM # 2	BATHROOM # 3
Aloe Vera lotion			
Bandages, assorted			
Bandage, elastic			
Calamine lotion			
Cotton balls, cotton swabs			
Cream, hydrocortisone or first aid cream			
Emergency telephone numbers			
First aid manual			
Gauze dressing			
Gauze pads			
Hydrogen peroxide			
Ice bag or ice pack			
Insect repellent			
Needle			
Ointment, antibiotic			
Safety pins			
Scissors			
Sunburn cream			
Tape, adhesive			
Thermometer			
Tongue depressors			
Tweezers			

MEDICATIONS

Medications	BATHROOM # 1	BATHROOM # 2	BATHROOM # 3
Analgesic, aspirin			
Antihistamine or decongestant			
Cough drops			
Eye drops, artificial tears			
Ipecac syrup			
Nose drops			
Pain reliever			
Prescription medications			
Throat spray			
Vitamins or herbal remedies			

SEWING KIT

Pick and Choose and what is best for your needs

A basic sewing kit includes a needle, a spool of white thread, about 3 buttons and some scissors.
That should fix most emergencies.

➡ Buttons (Different sizes and colors)	➡ Sewing basket or container
➡ Elastic	➡ Tape measure
➡ Hook and eyes	➡ Thimble
➡ Marking pencil	➡ Thread (Black, White and a few colors)
➡ Needles (sharps)	➡ Velcro™
➡ Pins, safety	➡ Yardstick
➡ Pins, straight	➡ Extras
➡ Scissors	➡
➡	➡

TOOL KIT

Pick and Choose and what is best for your needs

➡ Chisel	➡ Saw (crosscut, hacksaw, etc.)
➡ Drill, electric	➡ Scissors
➡ Duct tape	➡ Screwdriver, Flathead
➡ File	➡ Screwdriver, Phillips
➡ Flashlight	➡ Screwdriver, rechargeable
➡ Gloves	➡ Screws
➡ Hammer	➡ Staple gun
➡ Level	➡ Tape measure
➡ Lubricating oil or spray	➡ Toilet plunger
➡ Nails	➡ Utility knife with blade replacements
➡ Nuts and bolts	➡ Washers
➡ Paint equipment	➡ Wrenches
➡ Pliers (needle nose, slip joint, etc.)	➡ And store it in a Toolbox
➡ Sandpaper	➡
➡	➡
➡	➡
➡	➡
➡	➡

FURNITURE AND MISCELLANEOUS

Soft Stuff: (Usually made of fabric)	Hard Stuff: (Usually made of wood or metal)
Chair, for desk	Appliances (dishwasher, microwave, stove, refrigerator)
Chairs, for living room	Armoires for clothes or electronic equipment
Couch	Bookcases
Mattress and box springs (plus all the bedding: Bedspread / Blankets / Dust ruffle / Mattress pad / Pillow / Pillow cases / Shams / Sheets)	Chairs and kitchen or dining area
Rugs, carpet	Desk or computer table
	Dressers or drawers
Miscellaneous: For a complete list, go to First Move From Home	Entertainment center
Computer and accessories	Hutch or buffet for dishes
Telephones, answering machine, FAX machine	Lamps for living area and bedroom
Television, VCR, Electronic game system	Shelving
	Table, for kitchen or dining area
	Tables for living area and bedrooms

If you had to evacuate, many of these items would be essential until you could return home. It's also smart to keep these items in your house in case you get stranded from the outside world.

HOME EMERGENCY KIT

ITEMS TO BUY FOR EMERGENCY	WHERE IT IS STORED (Basement, Luggage, Box, Garage, Etc.)	COST OF ITEM	MARK OFF WHEN PURCHASED
Blanket, Bedding, Sleeping Bag			
Buckets for water and waste			
Candles, long-burning			
Can opener			
Canteen			
Clothing			
Fire extinguisher			
First aid kit			
Flashlight with batteries			
Food, non-refrigerated (3 days)			
Fuel for heating and cooking			
Garbage bags			
Knife			
Lamps, oil or battery			
Lantern			
Matches (waterproofed)			
Money, cash, credit cards			
Pots and pans			
Radio, AM/FM with batteries			
Rope			
Soap, hand and laundry			
Shovel			
Stove for cooking or			

ITEMS TO BUY FOR EMERGENCY	WHERE IT IS STORED (Basement, Luggage, Box, Garage, Etc.)	COST OF ITEM	MARK OFF WHEN PURCHASED
heating			
Telephone numbers			
Tent			
Tissue, facial and toilet			
Toilet, portable			
Towels, paper and cloth			
Utensils for cooking (Spatula, spoon, knife, fork)			
Utensils for eating (Plates, cups, flatware)			
Water in containers			
Water purification tablets			

FIRST MOVE AWAY FROM HOME

First time away from home? This list is for you. Everything you need to get started away from your home base. This is a basic list for single people either going to college to live in a dorm or starting out in a first apartment.

• Address book	• Medicine (Eye / Nose / Stomach / Throat / Pain Reliever/ Prescriptions
• Alarm clock / clock radio	• Microwave
• Answering machine / Telephone / Caller ID	• Office supplies (Dictionary / Highlighters / Notebooks / Paper / Paper clips / Pencils & Sharpener / Pens / Paper punch / Ruler/ Scissors / Stapler / Tape and dispenser)
• Backpack / Suitcases	• Papers (Automobile / Drivers license / Financial aid / Housing / Identification / Insurance (Auto and Medical) / Registration
• Batteries for all devices you pack	• Personal grooming supplies (toiletries)
• Bed linens (Bedspread / Blankets / Dust ruffle / Mattress pad / Pillow / Pillow cases / Shams / Sheets)	• Pictures (decorative or family and friends) and posters
• Bicycle / Lock	• Popcorn popper
• Blow dryer / Curling iron	• Pots and pans
• Books / Bookcase	• Plants
• Bulletin board / Push pins/ Dry erase board	• Refrigerator/Mini refrigerator
• Calendar / Planning book / Scheduling book	• Sewing kit
• Calling card for telephone long distance	• Shoe racks
• Camera / Film / Tripod	• Shower curtain / Bath mat / Shower caddy
• Cleaning supplies (Bags / Broom / Cleansers / Dustpan / Mop / Paper towels/ Rags / Sponge / Toilet bowl cleaner)	• Sport equipment
• Clothes / Jewelry / Shoes	• Stereo / CD player / CDs or cassette tapes
• Coffee pot / Hot chocolate maker	• Storage boxes/ Underneath bed boxes
• Computer / Printer / Scanner	• Telephone

• Dishes (Bowls / Cups / Flatware / Glasses / Pitcher / Plates)	• Television set / VCR / Game player
• Extension cords / Power strips	• Tools
• Fan	• Towels / Wash cloths / Shower cap
• First aid kit	• Umbrella
• Food (Drinks and Snacks)	• Utensils (Fork / Knife / Measuring cup & spoons / Spatula/ Spoons /
• Games	• Waste basket
• Hangers for clothes	
• Iron / Ironing board	
• Keys and key ring	
• Lamps (Desk / Floor / Night light / Table)	
• Laundry bag / Basket	
• Laundry supplies (Clothes pins / Detergent / Dryer sheets / Softener / Stain remover)	

Some things you might like to know:

1. You can raise a bed with a cinder block under each leg and lift it up high enough off the floor so plastic drawers or boxes will fit underneath.
2. Halogen lamps have been banned in some dorms because they are too hot and have caused fires.
3. Also banned some places are space heaters and hot plates since anything with exposed coils can catch on fire, especially in a small room where fabric from curtains or bedding is close to the appliance.
4. Some dorm room beds require extra long, twin sheets. Check on that before purchasing bedding.
5. Before you leave home, do a clean out of old papers and memories that were fun at the time, but they are in the past. Clutter reduction is vital.
6. When mounting items on walls, use sticky putty or the new, removable strips

HOUSEHOLD INVENTORY

Category or room inventoried on this page_____

DESCRIBE ITEM / SERIAL NUBER	PURCHASE DATE	PURCHASE PRICE	APPRAISAL PRICE	SPECIAL NOTES

Inventory by Category, e. g.: Electronics, Furniture, Appliances, Books, Household Goods OR Inventory by room: Living room, Kitchen, Master Bedroom. Take a video camera and video each room, telling about the item. Then record a description and serial number on this Inventory List.

AUTOMOBILE MAINTENANCE

Men used to take care of the cars. It was an unwritten rule since men were thought to be more mechanically minded. Rules changed and full-service gasoline stations died and made us all become participants in the upkeep of our cars whether we were prepared or not. Now anyone who drives a car needs a vague idea of what is listed in the maintenance manual for their auto.

The manual which comes with the car may be a guide to automobile maintenance, but if the work does not get scheduled on the calendar, it does not get completed. The Automobile Maintenance chart lends itself perfectly to maintenance on automobiles since most car maintenance manuals list an amount of months or miles between service recommendations. Service stations lube and tune-up shops try to put stickers on the doors with the date recorded of the last service provided. A few people may actually glance at these stickers once in a while, but not often enough to keep up with the service as advised by the service instruction book.

One of the chores specified is to fill the car with gasoline. People laugh when they see this chore listed, but it was included for those people who have trouble remembering to look at the gas gauge and often get stranded when the car runs out of gas. Schedule a certain day or days of the week to fill the gas tank and put it on your calendar to be marked off when it's done. If your car is still running out of gas, schedule a pit stop more frequently or less frequently if your tank is not down enough to be refilled. Most of us drive about the same amount of miles per week, so calendaring the days for gasoline refill is a handy way to recall that task.

Usually months elapse between oil or air filter changes. The Monthly-To-Do List, explained in **Section One** of this book, makes scheduling these chores a snap. For example, think about the weather in your area and you can guess what month you should have the snow tires put on or taken off. Think about the other chores you need to do to winterize your cars. Plan and schedule it all on the Weekly and Monthly Lists.

Once a month chores might include checking your tire pressure, refilling the windshield wiper solution, or checking the oil level. You know your cars. You schedule their maintenance to suit the needs of each auto. The **Automobile Maintenance List** has room to schedule one car, so print out more for all the cars in your household

You may want to keep a mileage list in your glove compartment to be updated when you refill the vehicle with gasoline. Buy a notebook and start the list. However, do not keep a mileage list if it becomes more trouble than support and fuel mileage stays constant between fill ups. Never get so many lists that they take over instead of benefiting you in planning your time.

Repairs cannot be planned since they are the surprise in our weekend plans. Although the repair manual never mentions the fact, autos have a built-in ability to plan break down at inconvenient times in the owner's life. As soon as the car starts the knock-knock-knocking, have it repaired and make the call before the whole gizmo falls apart in the middle of a blizzard, or a vacation or an emergency. This is a very basic list of maintenance items. Check with your mechanic for a full list specific to your automobile.

Auto Maintenance Section Includes These Lists:

TAKING CARE OF AN AUTOMOBILE

DEEP CLEAN VEHICLES

AUTO EMERGENCY KIT

TAKING CARE OF AN AUTOMOBILE

Type of Automobile_____ Year _____

Weight of Oil_____ Tire pressure_____

Grade of gasoline_____

CHORES TO BE DONE	Daily	Twice Weekly	Weekly	Twice Monthly	Monthly	Twice Yearly	3 Times Yearly	Yearly
BRAKES:								
Inspect brake pads and lining. Replace								
Turn drums, rotors. Replace linings								
Have bearings repacked								
Check fluid level in master cylinder								
TIRES:								
Rotate tires / Inspect tread for wear								
Check tire pressure (when tires are cold) and tire stem								
Have tires balanced/front end aligned								
Put on or take off snow tires								
FUEL: Carburetor, intake value, combustion chamber, injectors)								
Fill gasoline tank and add gasoline additives								
Replace fuel filter								
Perform tune-up/ spark plugs, filters								
BATTERY:								
Inspect battery and terminal cables. Clean & Tighten								
Adjust alternator belt. Check belt for cracks.								
OIL:								
Check oil level. Add if needed.								
Add fuel injection cleaner								
Change oil and oil filter (3,000/7,500 per spec.)								

CHORES TO BE DONE	Daily	Twice Weekly	Weekly	Twice Monthly	Monthly	Twice Yearly	3 Times Yearly	Yearly
EMISSION SYSTEM:								
Inspect exhaust pipes								
Have emission system and muffler checked. Have emission check for license plate renewal.								
LUBRICATION:								
Have chassis lubricated (if it has grease fittings)								
Lubricate lock cylinders, door hinges, moving body hinges.								
COOLING SYSTEM:								
Inspect fan belt.								
Check coolant/anti-freeze with hydrometer								
Flush radiator, cooling system. Add coolant or water								
Inspect radiator pressure cap, thermostat								
Inspect radiator hoses/bulging (upper & lower)								
HEATING SYSTEM:								
Inspect heater hoses and valves for clogs								
Have air-conditioning serviced/recharged								
WHEELS:								
Inspect axles and bearings								
Replace shock absorbers (leakage)								
Inspect lug nuts (bolts) & retighten on wheels								
TRANSMISSION:								
Check transmission fluid level. Add or change								
Check power-steering fluid level								
Adjust bands and linkage								
Inspect/Lube U-Joints								
LIGHTS:								
Check / Align headlights / Check horn								
Inspect and replace burned out bulbs								

CLEANING:								
Shampoo upholstery. Condition leather								
Vacuum interior. Change floor mats								
Wash outside. Wax. Clean wheels. Check for body damage								
Wash windows								
Change wiper blades. Add washer fluid								
FLUIDS:								
Antifreeze / Coolants								
Automatic transmission fluid								
Brake fluid								
Power steering fluid								
Windshield wiper fluid								

DEEP CLEAN VEHICLES

This List helps clean anything you have that takes you around this world. That means anything from a truck to roller blades that need maintenance and repair. Assign each vehicle to column #1 through column #5. Check off the space when the work is completed.

To maintain my vehicles I need to:	Vehicle #1	#2	#3	#4	#5
Shampoo upholstery--Treat leather upholstery					
Vacuum interior					
Wash windows--inside and outside					
Wash outside of vehicle					
Clean or repair wheels, hubcaps, tires					
Empty ashtrays, seat pockets					
Clean glove (accessory) box					
Throw out expired insurance & registration papers					
Put in current insurance & registration papers					
Put in maps, travel guides					
Have extra keys made--keep in safe place					
Clean steering wheels, dashboards, side slots					
Add first aid / Emergency kit					
Clean out trunk (boot) Vacuum					
Set up file for each vehicle--find & file important papers					
Clean children's car seats					
To repair my vehicles I need to:					
Fix problems with vehicle--things that drive you crazy					
Replace low fluids					
Check brakes					
Follow manufacturer's maintenance schedule on vehicle					
Replace burned out light bulbs					
Get rid of vehicles that no longer work					
For your information, determine how you owe on each vehicle's loan & the maturity date.					

Keep one of these kits in each of your cars for the safety of your family and your friends. Choose which items you want to keep in your auto emergency kit. Pack them in a truck organizer or a box. A minimum kit should include items for changing a tire, jumping a battery and a few tools with a flashlight for quick fixes. Duct tape can fix hoses until you can get to an auto center.

AUTO EMERGENCY KIT

ITEMS TO BUY	CAR #1	CAR #2	CAR #3
Blanket (or space blanket)			
Cloth			
Fan belt			
Fire extinguisher			
First aid kit			
Flares or reflectors			
Flashlight			
Food (trail mix, granola, etc.)			
Fuses			
Jumper cables			
Oil			
Pliers			
Reflectors			
Screwdrivers			
Siphon pump			
Tape, duct			
Tire inflator			
Tire jack			
Tire, spare			
Water			
Wire			
Wrench			

ITEMS TO BUY	CAR #1	CAR #2	CAR #3
WINTER ADDITIONS			
Candle in can or aluminum foil with matches			
Clothing--hat, gloves, boots, coat			
Flag, red for antenna			
Ice scraper			
Shovel			
Traction material (kitty litter, sand)			
SUMMER ADDITIONS			
Sunscreen			
Umbrella for shade protection			
Water and more water			
Windshield shade			

FOOD

Meal Time Comes So Often

Cooks serve food three times a day, 365 days a year with snacks thrown in for good measure. Most of us love to eat yet not everyone enjoys the grocery shopping, unpacking and putting away the groceries, preparing the meals, and cleaning up after the table is filled with dirty dishes. Those three meals a day create work and we try to ignore the reality that those mealtimes will come along whether we're prepared or not. To get food on the table means starting with

RECIPES, then
　　　　MENU PLANNING,
　　　　　　BUYING, and
　　　　　　　　STORAGE. The actual
　　　　　　　　　　PREPARATION is last.

Don't try to plan meals unless you have an idea what recipes you are able to cook, bake or stew to get a meal on the table. If you have basic recipes, the next step is menu planning. Then comes buying the food and putting it away before you start food preparation.

Is it a chore to get food on the table for all those meals? Yes! It is work and it takes time. That is reality. It is also reality that you get hungry. So to coordinate those two absolutes means accepting the inevitable and planning ahead.

Chances are you have no idea what to fix and no idea what usable food is stored in your pantry. Back to basics. Start with what you know and understand. Build a foundation of simple recipes and a simple plan and branch out later.

You are going to SUBDIVIDE your meal planning into small increments that you can control. Food can be very simple or elaborately planned. Those kitchen gourmets who love to cook can plan far ahead and feel in control as they never have before. Perhaps deli-prepared foods and microwave heated foods are your idea of cooking. You can plan those menus so you know what is available and ready to be heated up or tossed together.

The first section is about recipes—a vital part of meal planning.

Food Section Includes These Instructions and Lists::

Recipes—My Brain Has No Ideas For Dinner

MAIN DISHES YOU CAN COOK

SIDE DISHES YOU CAN COOK

Planning—Mom Had a Plan—I Guess I Need a Plan

EASIEST MENU PLANNER

WEEKLY MENU PLANNER

Buying—It's Time to Go to the Grocery Store

WEEKLY GROCERY LIST ALPHABETICAL CHECK OFF

WEEKLY GROCERY LIST CATEGORY WRITE IN

STORE ADVERTISEMENTS

GROCERY STORE AD COMPARISON

COUPONS FOR SAVING—WORTH IT OR NOT

REBATE LIST

Storage—How to Organize the Food in the Cupboards

Preparation—Checklist for Meal Preparation

IT'S A FEAST!--SPECIAL EVENT MEAL PLANNER

Food Recipes

My Brain has No Ideas for Dinner

◊ **First solution**--gather some recipes that make your mouth water. Printed recipes will take over the world one day. People of all ages, cultures and nationalities love to collect recipes. They are printed in newspapers, magazines and best selling cook books.

Recipes are passed down from generation to generation. Children returning home usually have favorite food dishes they want mother to recreate for them. Family and friends always have recipes to share. When someone fixes a food you like, ask for the recipe. Sometimes they'll say "No." But most of the time they'll hand you the card and say, "Here it is. Copy it for yourself and enjoy."

We love to eat and we love to eat certain types of food. Yet our tastes may change and then we collect new types of recipes. Most cooks are on the trail of new and tastier recipes that will satisfy food cravings.

Major corporations sponsor food competitions because there are so many recipe-hunters in the world exploring printed words looking for "add 1 cup of this and 2 teaspoons of that." Food corporations love to print cook books involving their products since these low cost books mean you will buy their products as ingredients in your cooking.

Now we have established that you will have no trouble finding recipes, we must acknowledge another problem. What do you do with all these recipes once you have them? You need a system for organizing your recipes.

◊ **Second solution**--organize your recipes. You might be a recipe card enthusiast, cutting and pasting all those recipes onto cards and filing them by category in a large file box. You may tear out recipes and throw them into a shoe box hoping to look through them one day and actually try some. You might be a cook book collector with a new book following you home from every trip to the grocery store. And you might read recipes in your spare time as a relaxing hobby.

So why are you one of the people who fix the same meals over and over? You know the answer. You can never find the recipe you need. And when you do have the recipe in hand, you don't have all the ingredients to fix the food. Lost recipes and missing ingredients. Somehow it becomes easier to just fix meals from whatever you have on hand and is familiar.

The best way to organize on paper is a three-ring binder made to hold photographs. Small-sized recipes on paper or cards may be slipped under the magnetic, plastic sheets and easily read through the transparent plastic. Larger pages, 8 1/2 x 11", may be hole punched and hooked on the binder rings. Recipe cards may also be put into pre-formed photograph slots if you have a few of the slip in the pocket type photograph sheets. IMPORTANT--Purchase a good quality book with high quality plastic sheets or your recipes will get stuck inside pages that will not open to release the paper. Low grade plastic tends to "grab" paper and not let go.

◊ **Third solution**--categorize your recipes. Divide the binder into sections using index separators and arrange the recipes according to the <u>main ingredient</u> or <u>type</u>. Main categories could include Beef, Chicken, Fish, Vegetables (<u>Main ingredients</u>) or Soup, Salad, Desserts, Chinese

(<u>Types</u>). Choose categories that fit your food tastes. Don't make a category for seafood if you never eat fish. Make your own tabs for the categories with sticky note paper or buy heavy weight paper with pre-made tabs.

◊ **Long range solution**--add a binder as your collection grows. At first one binder may be all you need. Next you'll find you have two types of recipes--those you love and are tried and treasured and those you'd like to attempt for a future meal. Put the old reliable recipes into a <u>Favorite Recipes Binder</u> and make a second titled <u>New Recipes to Try Binder</u>.

When a new recipe is clipped, file it in your New Recipes Binder before it is lost. After it has been tested, add the tasty recipe cards to the Favorite Recipe Binder. Throw the cards with meals that tasted horrible into the trash. Each cook in the house may want their own recipe binder. Then when cooks take turns sautéing food, it's easy to find recipes. And when someone leaves home, their recipe book is ready for their own kitchen.

Cook books have so many mouth-watering recipes and you will want to transfer some of them to your binder. You don't want to tear pages out of the books. Either hand copy or machine copy recipes-to-try and slip them into your New Recipes Binder.

◊ **Planning solution**--as you sit down to plan your meals, remember to use recipes from both binders. Design your favorite menus and transfer them to a *Permanent Menu List* published by List Organizer so you don't forget where they are. You may even clip recipes to the bottom of the *Permanent Menu List*. Or at each planning session, flip through your binders looking for meal ideas.

Instead of sitting in a box, new recipes will tried and evaluated. Use your New Recipes to Try Binder to add new spirit to your boring meals. Then after testing, either put recipes into the Favorite Binder or toss them out. And favorite recipes will be used sparingly so they don't become stale from appearing on the menu too often.

◊ **Yearly solution**--revise your binders. Eventually you will limit recipes to some favorites and eliminate unwanted recipes as your tastes change or you realize you will not get around to testing so many recipes for months or years. When you reach the point that you have too many unwanted recipes, calendar a time on your planner or on the To-Do Lists to look through the binders and toss out recipes you don't want.

You might have to stop collecting for a while. Or, if collecting is the fun for you, toss out many recipes that sounded good 10 years ago but have lost the ability to spark your appetite. Add the newer, appetizing recipes. Never feel you have to try every recipe just because you took the time to clip it. It takes time and effort and money to try every meal idea.

Your children who liked spaghetti may have moved out. Or you're trying to lose weight and now you like salads. Tastes change. Members sitting around the table change. And so should the recipes in your binders.

Recipes--they are the backbone of your Plan. Without them you cannot go on to the next step which is Meal Planning. Even peanut butter sandwiches need a recipe. You might have that one memorized, but at some point you learned how to modify that recipe for sliced bread and peanut butter and jelly or banana or marshmallow fluff sandwiches. Now keep going and find some more recipes that you want to fix.

Let's begin by figuring out what recipes you know how to fix. Think about main dishes and side dishes you know how to prepare and write them down on the next two Lists--Main Dishes you can cook and Side Dishes you can cook.

Breakfast – Write down seven main dishes and seven side dishes. Example: Scrambled eggs & toast (One main dish and one side dish)

Lunch—Write down ten main dishes and ten side dishes. Example: Cheese sandwich & chips

Dinner—Write down eighteen main dishes and eighteen side dishes. Example: Hamburger, salad, baked potato (One main dish and two side dishes)

Think of at least <u>seven</u> main dishes for the meals you prepare and <u>seven</u> side dishes. This allows you to plan for one week of menus.

MAIN DISHES YOU CAN COOK

BREAKFAST MAIN DISHES YOU CAN COOK:	DINNER MAIN DISHES YOU CAN COOK:
1.	1.
2.	2.
3.	3.
4.	4.
5.	5.
6	6.
7.	7.
LUNCH MAIN DISHES YOU CAN COOK:	8.
1.	9.
2.	10.
3.	11.
4.	12.
5.	13.
6.	14.
7.	15.
8.	16.
9.	17.
10.	18.

Planning starts at this basic level. What do you know how to fix? A Hamburger; a Hot Dog; Spaghetti; Frozen Pizza; a Sandwich. Or if you are a real cook, you may list Quiche; Ratatouille; or Poached Salmon. Plan your meals and grocery list using these ideas. Sometimes just knowing what you are able to fix can help you get a good jump on meal planning. Now, put a big star by the items that you can fix in 15 minutes or less. You always need some very quick meals.

129

SIDE DISHES YOU CAN COOK

BREAKFAST SIDE DISHES YOU CAN COOK:	DINNER SIDE DISHES YOU CAN COOK:
1.	1.
2.	2.
3.	3.
4.	4.
5.	5.
6	6.
7.	7.
LUNCH SIDE DISHES YOU CAN COOK:	8.
1.	9.
2.	10.
3.	11.
4.	12.
5.	13.
6.	14.
7.	15.
8.	16.
9.	17.
10.	18.

On this list add vegetables, fruits, breads, pasta and rice side dishes.

Food Planning

Mom Had a Plan—I Guess I need a Plan

Yes, your Mom probably did have a plan. That plan helped her prepare hundreds of meals every year. It brought food into the house. It made sure there were after school snacks. It might have kept the cookie jar full. The kitchen plan kept things humming along in your Mom's kitchen. Do you need the same plan Mom devised? No. Do you need your own plan? Yes!

Now you've gathered and categorized some recipes and know what you can cook, you need to organize the recipes into menus. All menus start with a seven-day or one week plan. Food needs to be planned for a minimum of one week since it takes time to buy and store the food. Shopping for groceries once a week keeps you with plenty of food in the house and a food budget that is under control.

A beginning cook may want to have the same seven menus for a few weeks until menu planning becomes easier. Beginners may want to have spaghetti or steak or vegetable stew every Sunday for a month. Sometimes it is easier to cook the same meal on the same day of the week when starting out in menu planning.

One advantage to this is your grocery list stays the same each week and you become acquainted with the aisles in your grocery stores without feeling threatened. You are buying the same food each week and your shopping skills improve as you learn about house brands and grades of meat and what fruits are in season.

Or try a different food store each week for a month. Soon you will learn what stores have good values or what store fits your bakery or frozen food requirements. Stores are different. By shopping once a week and trying different stores, you master shopping skills. You save money. You save time shopping. You become a knowledgeable consumer. Wow! All that success takes place just because you started with a plan.

As cooking develops into a manageable skill the amateur cook may add variety to the menus by trying new recipes. Do this slowly. Do not try to cook seven new dinners in one week. You will become overwhelmed and try to avoid the kitchen. Try a new recipe once in a while. Stay with old favorites for most of your meals.

Your main dish might be a hamburger or a frozen dinner. Your side dish might be canned beans. Good. Write that down using the step-by-step meal planner in this book. After the blanks are filled in, a one week meal plan will magically appear. That's because a meal plan can add magic to your menus.

Expert cooks may plan two, three or four weeks ahead because they have many recipes and menu ideas. Structuring meals is natural to them. A main dish might be shrimp gumbo or beef stroganoff. Make your menu choices according to your cooking level. All grades of cooks may use menu planning to their advantage.

Organize your meals around the yearly sales. Professional menu makers know that blueberries are inexpensive in July and they save their blueberry recipes until summer. Organize meals around your schedule. Keep everyday meals simple during the holiday season. New parents need to simplify meals. Plan crock pot or oven meals during work days. Include a "soup and sandwich" meal for busy days.

Think of elaborate meals when the table is surrounded by loving friends or family and it is time for a feast. A special meal planner for large meals is **It's a Feast!** included in this book.

Do you like to include a meal at a restaurant during the week? Then only plan six main meals and plan your night out as your seventh meal. Does your kitchen stay quiet during the day while everyone is gone to work or school? Then only plan main or evening meals for the week. However, if you pack lunches for the group, write out menus and buy food to keep those lunch sacks full.

Your needs are different than mine or Mom's. That is why my plan won't work for you and Mom's plan won't help you either. You need your own plan. Think about your needs. Do you eat the same items for breakfast each day? Do you grab lunch at a restaurant? Do you have a full table every night or do you eat alone? And if you have an empty table tonight will it be full for the weekend when everyone drops by your house?

Meal planning takes a little guess work. Just when you thought every family member would be home for your well-prepared meal, they all have last minute plans. And then they all show up when you were planning a simple, quick meal. That is part of cooking. However, having a plan and food in the house allows you to be flexible. Any menu plan needs to be flexible. Adapt your plan to your needs. And if it doesn't work this week, try again next week. Make a few modifications. And keep planning. You will end up with your first weekly blueprint for meals. It's a piece of cake.

For beginning cooks I've invented the **Easiest Menu Planner** with space for three meals a day, one main dish and including up to two side dishes. This is a one week menu planner.

EASIEST MENU PLANNER (Sample)

Sunday: Main Dish	Side Dish	Side Dish

For more advanced cooks and for those who like to plan their grocery items along with their menus, I've invented the **Weekly Menu Planning List** with space for a main meal including one main dish, three side dishes and the grocery ingredients needed to prepare each item. There is also space for an extra meal with one main dish and one side item and the grocery items you need.

WEEKLY MENU PLANNER (Sample)

This list is for advanced menu planners or those with more complex menus..

MONDAY, Main Meal   **TUESDAY, Main Meal**

MAIN DISH	Grocery Item	Grocery Item	Grocery Item	MAIN DISH	Grocery Item	Grocery Item	Grocery Item
SIDE DISH				SIDE DISH			

Fill in one of the Menu Planners (either the Easiest or the Weekly) using
Main Dishes I can cook List and
Side Dishes I can cook List

EASIEST MENU PLANNER

Sunday: Main Dish	Side Dish	Side Dish
Monday: Main Dish	Side Dish	Side Dish
Tuesday: Main Dish	Side Dish	Side Dish
Wednesday: Main Dish	Side Dish	Side Dish
Thursday: Main Dish	Side Dish	Side Dish
Friday: Main Dish	Side Dish	Side Dish
Saturday: Main Dish	Side Dish	Side Dish
Extra Meal: Main Dish	Side Dish	Side Dish

Put this on your refrigerator and use it to plan your grocery list. Remember- Plan your Meals, Plan Your Grocery List, Buy Groceries, Make Good Meals.

This is a good list for beginning meal planners or those who have simpler menus.

SAMPLE MENU PLANNER

This illustrates how to fill out the Weekly Menu Planner. Adapt it to fit your lifestyle. If you are planning to go out for dinner on Tuesday, enter that in the Tuesday, Main Meal.

MONDAY, Main Meal   TUESDAY, Main Meal

MAIN DISH *Chicken Quesadilla*	Grocery Item Chicken	Grocery Item Flour tortillas	Grocery Item Cheese, onions	MAIN DISH *Tuna salad*	Grocery Item Tuna, Tomato	Grocery Item Celery, Pickle	Grocery Item Mayonnaise
SIDE DISH *Refried Beans*	Can of refried bean	Cheese		SIDE DISH *Roll*	Store Roll	Butter	
SIDE DISH *Fruit*	Strawberries			SIDE DISH *Apple*	Apple		
DESSERT *Ice cream*	Ice Cream			DESSERT *Brownie*	Buy store brownies		

MONDAY, Extra Meals   (Breakfast)   TUESDAY, Extra Meals (Lunch for kids)

MAIN DISH *Eggs/Bacon*	Grocery Item Eggs	Grocery Item Bacon	Grocery Item	MAIN DISH *Sandwich*	Grocery Item Turkey	Grocery Item Cheese	Grocery Item Bread
SIDE DISH *Toast*	Bread	Butter	Jelly	SIDE DISH *Chips / Fruit*	Corn chips	Banana	Carton of juice

WEEKLY MENU PLANNER

MONDAY, Main Meal   **TUESDAY, Main Meal**

MAIN DISH	Grocery Item	Grocery Item	Grocery Item	MAIN DISH	Grocery Item	Grocery Item	Grocery Item
SIDE DISH				SIDE DISH			
SIDE DISH				SIDE DISH			
DESSERT				DESSERT			

MONDAY, Extra Meals   **TUESDAY, Extra Meals**

MAIN DISH	Grocery Item	Grocery Item	Grocery Item	MAIN DISH	Grocery Item	Grocery Item	Grocery Item
SIDE DISH				SIDE DISH			

LISTS FOR MUDDLE MANAGEMENT

WEDNESDAY, Main Meal

MAIN DISH	Grocery Item	Grocery Item	Grocery Item
SIDE DISH			
SIDE DISH			
DESSERT			

THURSDAY, Main Meal

MAIN DISH	Grocery Item	Grocery Item	Grocery Item
SIDE DISH			
SIDE DISH			
DESSERT			

WEDNESDAY, Extra Meal

MAIN DISH	Grocery Item	Grocery Item	Grocery Item
SIDE DISH			

THURSDAY, Extra Meal

MAIN DISH	Grocery Item	Grocery Item	Grocery Item
SIDE DISH			

FRIDAY, Extra Meal

MAIN DISH	Grocery Item	Grocery Item	Grocery Item
SIDE DISH			

SATURDAY, Extra Meal

MAIN DISH	Grocery Item	Grocery Item	Grocery Item
SIDE DISH			

FRIDAY, Main Meal   **SATURDAY, Main Meal**

MAIN DISH	Grocery Item	Grocery Item	Grocery Item	MAIN DISH	Grocery Item	Grocery Item	Grocery Item
SIDE DISH				SIDE DISH			
SIDE DISH				SIDE DISH			
DESSERT				DESSERT			

SUNDAY, Main Meal   **SUNDAY, Extra Meal**

MAIN DISH	Grocery Item	Grocery Item	Grocery Item	MAIN DISH	Grocery Item	Grocery Item	Grocery Item
SIDE DISH				SIDE DISH			
SIDE DISH				SIDE DISH			
DESSERT				DESSERT			

Food Buying

It's Time to go to the Grocery Store

Grocery stores or food markets are filled with thousands of items. No shopper has the intellectual capacity to enter a modern supermarket and try to remember all the products to purchase. Cartoonists earn money making fun of characters trying to memorize a shopping list. You've seen the cartoon character struggling to recall why he came to the super market and forgetting to buy half the items he needed. It isn't funny when it happens to you.

The variety of food in these markets is fantastic. The square footage to be covered by your shopping cart is immense. Yet shoppers rush into the store everyday without an idea in the world what to buy except they know they are out of bread and milk. Then they leave with a grocery sack filled with food and nothing to fix for dinner.

Five minutes of writing a grocery list would save frustration, money and time. Yet people don't bother because they are in a hurry. Sometimes the lists they make are not helpful. Maybe you are going about organizing a shopping list in the wrong way.

There are two ways to build a grocery shopping list. One way is to write down what you want to buy. You get a piece of paper and a pencil and scribble down what you will buy. Then you add a list of products you've used at home. This is the Add or Write In method.

The second system uses a master grocery list. It lists a majority of items to buy at the grocery store. When you plan your meals, transfer your meal ingredients to the master list and include the extra products you need to buy. This is the Subtract method

The Add method means writing down what you need or adding it to your grocery list. The Subtract method means keeping a huge list of everything you use and subtracting what you need from the list by checking it off.

Grocery lists may have given you trouble because you tried the Add method when you needed to try the Subtract method. List Organizer publishes three styles of grocery lists.

List Organizer developed Three Styles of Grocery Lists:

◊ *Alphabetical Check Off*--ingredients listed alphabetically (<u>Subtract Method</u>)
(Included in this book)

◊ *Category Check Off*--ingredients categorized, then listed alphabetically
(<u>Subtract Method</u>) Corresponds to sections or aisles in your store.
Pads are available for purchase from List Organizer.

◊ *Category Write In*--nineteen categories with a space underneath for your
personalized written grocery list (<u>Add Method</u>) Corresponds to sections or aisles in your store (Included in this book)

Try all three styles until you decide which one you like best. After you choose your favorite, refills are available for purchase from List Organizer printed in color, pads of 25 sheets. On the back of the Grocery Lists are Health and Beauty products and the Compare Grocery Ads List.

Keep the list accessible on your refrigerator or in your planning notebook. Write on the list what you need at the grocery store. When you plan your menus, transfer the required ingredients to the list.

When you go to the grocery store take:

➢ Grocery List / Compare List
➢ Coupons
➢ Calculator (if you like to add food totals as you shop)
➢ Grocery store advertisements
➢ Grocery bags to be recycled

WEEKLY GROCERY LIST

ALPHABETICAL CHECK OFF

∇ <u>Apples</u> __	∇ Cheese, cottage__	∇ Fruit, canned__	∇ Mexican food__	∇ Pudding__	∇ <u>Tea</u> __
∇ Applesauce__	∇ Cheese, parmesan__	∇ Fruit, dried__	∇ Milk__	∇ Pumpkin__	∇ Tomato paste__
∇ <u>Baby Food</u> __	∇ Cheese, sliced__	∇ Fruit, fresh__	∇ Muffins__	∇ <u>Raisins</u> __	∇ Tomato sauce__
∇ Baby Formula__	∇ Cheese, spread__	∇ Fruit, frozen__	∇ Mushrooms__	∇ Ravioli__	∇ Tomatoes, canned__
∇ Bacon__	∇ Cherries__	∇ <u>Garlic</u> __	∇ Mustard__	∇ Relish__	∇ Tomatoes, fresh__
∇ Bagels__	∇ Chicken__	∇ Gelatin__	∇ <u>Noodles / Pasta</u>	∇ Rice__	∇ Tortillas__
∇ Bakery goods__	∇ Chili__	∇ Graham crackers__	∇ Noodle, mix__	∇ Rice, mix__	∇ Tuna__
∇ Baking powder__	∇ Chili beans__	∇ Granola bars__	∇ Nuts__	∇ <u>Salad dressings</u> __	∇ Turkey__
∇ Baking soda__	∇ Chinese food__	∇ Grapefruit__	∇ <u>Oatmeal</u> __	∇ Salt__	∇ <u>Vanilla</u> __
∇ Bananas__	∇ Chips, potato__	∇ Gravy__	∇ Oil__	∇ Sauce, Barbecue__	∇ Vegetables canned__
∇ Beans__	∇ Chips, tortilla__	∇ Green pepper__	∇ Olives__	∇ Sauce, Chili__	∇ Vegetables frozen__
∇ Beans, refried__	∇ Chocolate, baking__	∇ Gum__	∇ Onion__	∇ Sauce, Enchilada__	∇ Vinegar__
∇ Beef, hamburger__	∇ Chocolate chips__	∇ <u>Ham</u> __	∇ Onion rings__	∇ Sauce, Hot__	∇ <u>Waffles, frozen</u> __
∇ Beef jerky__	∇ Cocoa__	∇ Honey__	∇ Oranges__	∇ Sauce, Pasta__	∇ Water__
∇ Beef, roast__	∇ Cocoa mix__	∇ Hot dogs__	∇ <u>Pancake mix</u> __	∇ Sauce, Picante__	∇ Worcestershire__
∇ Beef, steak__	∇ Coconut__	∇ <u>Ice, block, cube</u> __	∇ Peaches__	∇ Sauce, Sloppy Joe__	∇ <u>Yams</u> __
∇ Beer__	∇ Coffee__	∇ Ice cream__	∇ Peanut butter__	∇ Sauce, Soy__	∇ Yeast__
∇ Beets__	∇ Cookies__	∇ Ice cream cones__	∇ Pears__	∇ Sauce, Steak__	∇ Yogurt__
∇ Berries__	∇ Cooking spray__	∇ Ice cream toppings__	∇ Peas__	∇ Sauce, Tartar__	**Extras:**
∇ Biscuit mix__	∇ Corn__	∇ <u>Jam/Jelly</u> __	∇ Pepper__	∇ Sauerkraut__	
∇ Biscuits/rolls__	∇ Corn meal__	∇ Juice, bottled__	∇ Pickles__	∇ Sausage__	
∇ Bouillon cubes__	∇ Cornstarch__	∇ Juice, frozen__	∇ Pie__	∇ Seafood__	
∇ Bread crumbs__	∇ Corn syrup__	∇ <u>Ketchup</u> __	∇ Pie crust__	∇ Seasoning mix__	
∇ Bread, French__	∇ Crackers__	∇ <u>Lemons</u> __	∇ Pie filling__	∇ Shortening__	
∇ Bread__	∇ Cream cheese__	∇ Lemon juice__	∇ Pineapple__	∇ Soda pop__	
∇ Broccoli__	∇ Cream, non-dairy__	∇ Lettuce__	∇ Pizza, dough__	∇ Soup, canned__	
∇ Buns__	∇ Cream, whipping__	∇ Limes__	∇ Pizza, frozen__	∇ Soup, dry__	
∇ Butter__	∇ Croutons__	∇ Lunch meat__	∇ Pizza, sauce__	∇ Sour cream__	
∇ <u>Cabbage</u> __	∇ Cucumber__	∇ <u>Macaroni</u> __	∇ Plums__	∇ Spaghetti__	
∇ Cake__	∇ <u>Dessert</u> __	∇ Mandarin oranges__	∇ Popcorn__	∇ Spices__	
∇ Cake/brownie mix__	∇ Dips__	∇ Margarine__	∇ Pork and beans__	∇ Stew__	
∇ Candy__	∇ Drink mix__	∇ Marshmallows__	∇ Potatoes__	∇ Stuffing__	
∇ Carrots__	∇ <u>Eggs</u> __	∇ Mayonnaise__	∇ Potatoes, dried__	∇ Sugar, brown__	
∇ Celery__	∇ Evaporated milk__	∇ Meat, canned__	∇ Pot pies__	∇ Sugar, powdered__	
∇ Cereal__	∇ <u>Fish</u> __	∇ Meat, fresh__	∇ Poultry__	∇ Sugar, white__	
∇ Cheese, block__	∇ Flour__	∇ Melon__	∇ Pretzels__	∇ Syrup__	

HOUSEHOLD / HEALTH AND BEAUTY LIST

• Air freshener	• Dishwasher soap	• Plastic utensils	• Hair color
• Aluminum foil	• Fabric softener	• Plastic wrap	• Hair mousse / gel
• Ammonia	• Film	• Scrubber / scourer	• Hair spray
• Auto supplies	• Furniture polish	• Starch	• Lotion
• Bags, Lunch	• Glass cleaner	• Straws	• Mouthwash
• Bag, Sandwich	• Insecticides	• Toilet bowl cleaner	• Pain reliever
• Bag, Storage	• Kitty litter	• Toothpicks	• Pantyhose
• Bag, Trash	• Laundry detergent	• Wax	• Razor blades
• Bag, Vacuum	• Laundry pre-wash	• Wax paper	• Shampoo / conditioner
• Batteries	• Light bulbs	• Extras:	• Shaving cream
• Bleach	• Matches	•	• Toilet tissue
• Broom	• Mop	•	• Tooth brush
• Candles	• Napkins	• HEALTH & BEAUTY	• Tooth paste
• Cards	• Oven cleaner	• Aspirin	• Wet wipes
• Carpet cleaner	• Paper cups	• Bandages	• Extras:
• Charcoal	• Paper napkins	• Cold remedies	•
• Cleaner	• Paper plates	• Deodorant	•
• Cleanser	• Paper towels	• Diapers	•
• Detergent, laundry	• Pet food	• Eye care	•
•	•	• Facial tissue	•
•	•	• Feminine hygiene	•

WEEKLY GROCERY LIST
Category Write In

1. Bakery Goods	2. Baking Supplies	3. Beverages
4. Candy / Snacks	**5. Canned / Boxed Goods**	**6. Cereal**
7. Condiments / Jelly	**8. Dairy**	**9. Deli / Prepared Foods**
10. Frozen Foods	**11. Fruits**	**12. Health / Beauty**
13. Meat / Poultry / Fish	**14. Noodles / Pasta / Rice**	**15. Paper Goods**
16. Pet Food	**17. Soap / Cleaning Products**	**18. Spices**
19. Vegetables	**Extras**	**Extras**

Store Advertisements

Use this section only if you use advertisements to compare prices.

Grocery stores, discount stores, or any retail store will advertise a sale. It is part of the selling game. Everyone loves a bargain if getting the bargain is easy. Do you throw out the weekly grocery store advertisements with the trash? I can guess the reason--it takes too much time to read the ads or you like to shop at the same store. You must be rolling in cash since you do not need to save money on items you buy each week. What? You could stand to save some money on groceries. Read on.

The **Grocery Store Ad List** lets you quickly write down and compare weekly advertisements. Most grocery store ads expire after seven days, so planning before buying is very important to take advantage of the sales. The compare list gives you a quick method for comparing prices between different stores. This chart must be filled out at home before you enter the store.

Look at the menus you have devised and find one where the ingredients for the recipes correspond to items on sale. Keep it simple. There is no need to spend hours planning meals to fit all the advertisements each week or to use all the coupons you have to redeem. Try to purchase your major or expensive ingredients on sale and change your menus a little to take advantage of the market fluctuations. Menu plans can be shifted to take advantage of weekly sales. Advertisements can be unacceptable if they encourage you to purchase sale items that you cannot use.

HOW TO USE LIST

1. Collect all the grocery store advertisements.

2. a. Compare your pre-arranged menus and the ingredients needed with the ads. OR
   b. Arrange your menus around the items that are on sale.

3. At the top of the **Grocery Store Compare Ads List** fill in the names of the supermarkets whose prices you are comparing.

4. Using the advertisements, fill in the items you are comparing with the brands and prices underneath each store's heading. (Example: Store #1, Apples $1.00 per pound; Store #3 Apples $1.19 per pound)

5. Circle the least expensive item, indicating where you should buy that ingredient.

6. Use the completed list as a shopping list for each store. Or use it to help you decide which store to shop at this week.

(This list can be modified to compare weekly advertisements by discount or retail stores that are in competition with one another.)

GROCERY STORE AD COMPARISON

TYPE OF FOOD	STORE	STORE	STORE	STORE
BABY GOODS				
BAKERY				
BAKING SUPPLIES				
BEVERAGES				
CANDY/SNACKS				
CANNED/BOXED GOODS				
CEREALS				
CONDIMENTS/JELLY				
COOKIES/CRACKER				
DAIRY				
DELI/PREPARED FOODS				
FROZEN FOODS				
FRUITS				
HEALTH/BEAUTY				
MEAT/POULTRY/FISH				
NOODLES/PASTA/RICE				
PAPER GOODS				
PET FOOD				
SOAPS/CLEANING				
SPICES				
VEGETABLES				

Coupons for Saving—Worth it or

Coupon clipping takes organization. Coupon filing takes organization. Coupon redeeming takes organization. That may be the reason that approximately 4% of all coupons marketed are actually redeemed. When Kraft Foods starts handing out quarters at the supermarket, we will all be in line. When they hand out that quarter in the form of a coupon (which may be doubled to fifty-cents by the store) people ignore the offer. Why? We cannot find the time to clip, file and redeem. What that means is we do not have time to set up an organization system for coupons.   Even a casual coupon clipper needs a storage arrangement since those little pieces of paper get lost or destroyed. A storage file protects coupons and makes them easy to retrieve.

There are many ways to file coupons: <u>alphabetically; expiration date; product category; grocery store aisles</u>. Each has pluses and minuses. It depends on your preference.

The <u>Alphabetical </u>format starts with index dividers labeled from A-Z. Coupons are filed either by product name or brand name. Be consistent. For example, Bride's applesauce could be filed under B for Bride (brand name) or under A for applesauce (product name).

The <u>Expiration</u> date format begins with 12 dividers, one for each month of the year. Coupons are filed according to the month in which they expire which is usually listed at the top of the coupon.   The shopper uses the November expiration date coupons during the November shopping trips. The coupons with no expiration dates listed may be filed in with the other coupons or kept separately.

The <u>Product Category</u> system groups foods together using categories. The categories, such as paper products, soup, meat, are written on index dividers. Coupons are filed with the newer coupons at the back on each section. Then the coupons ready to expire are moved to the front of the category.

The supermarket <u>Aisle</u> system works if you shop at one store and redeem the majority of your coupons at that store. Obtain a layout of the grocery store or sketch one yourself. List what is stocked on the shelves in each aisle. Organize and label your coupon dividers to correspond to the aisles. This would be similar to the product category system since stores group similar products together. The difference is when you enter the store, the coupons are easy to pull out as you start at one side of the store and go back and forth on the aisles.

There are many commercial coupon file kits for sale or make your own using materials from an office supply store. All of these systems may be filed in a shoe box or check filing box (for larger collections), or a coupon wallet or notebook with sleeves (for the casual coupon user).

Clipping Coupons

Clipping coupons may be your downfall. The problem for you is getting them cut out and filed before they are lost.

1. Label a large manila envelope--COUPONS. In the envelope put magazine pages with coupons, newspaper pages with coupons, coupons mailed to you, and loose coupons.
2. On your calendar, schedule a block of time once a week (twice a month at the minimum) for coupon organization
3. Clip coupons stored in the COUPON envelope
4. File them according to the divider system you have designed.
5. Mark on the grocery shopping list which items have a redeemable coupon
6. For larger savings, read the supermarket advertisements and combine sale items with coupons.

Redeeming Coupons

This is easy--if you followed the instructions for clipping and filing coupons. The cashiers do not think it is humorous for you to throw your coupons on the counter and ask them to check if any of your coupons are useable on your purchase (although I have seen this method used.)

As you move through the store, compare your coupon with the brand name and size listed on each coupon. When you find the right product and put it in your basket, move the coupon to the front of the file in a holding area. When you reach the check out lane, take the coupons from the holding area of the file and give them to the cashier.

Of course, to be successful you have to remember to take the coupons with you into the store. When you go to the market remember: BE SURE TO TAKE ALONG YOUR GROCERY LIST and BE SURE TO TAKE ALONG YOUR COUPONS. Double check each time and soon it will be a habit.

Redeeming Rebates

Rebates are usually not instant money like coupons are. Receiving the rebates takes more organization. Usually you have to find a special form for the rebate; you need part of the product package as proof of purchase; you need the cash register receipt; and you need to mail it off to the clearinghouse and wait for the rebate to be returned in the form of check, cash or coupon. Redeeming rebates is for the patient and organized.

The REBATE LIST helps you remember what money you are trying to get back after buying products.

How to use the Rebate List

1. Schedule a time to work on sending out rebates
2. Collect a rebate form. File it in an envelope or alphabetical file.
3. Enter the name of the product.
4. Enter the address of the clearinghouse or company.
5. Check off on list:
    ➢ Proof of purchase
    ➢ Cash register receipt
    ➢ Miscellaneous needed for redemption
6. File these with the rebate form.
7. When you have all the needed forms, mail them.
8. List the date the rebate is mailed.
9. List the date the rebate money or coupon is returned.
10. Enjoy your money

REBATE LIST

PRODUCT NAME	MAILING ADDRESS	PROOF PURCH	STORE RECPT	MISC.	DATE MAIL	DATE RECVD

Food Storage

How to Organize the Food in the Cupboards

Food storage is number four in the "meal on the table" project. Now comes putting away the food after it's purchased. Sometimes this part comes when you are rushed for time and you might throw the food in a corner while shoving the perishables in the refrigerator and freezer. In the future, plan to buy the food when there is time to put the groceries away properly.

You will organize in one of two ways--Product Category or Menu Groupings. The Product Category method puts all the canned tomato products together, next to the canned fruits or the canned soups. Cereals, juices, and cake mixes would be arranged by group. Similar items sit next to each other in your cupboards. It's the same way a super market organizes their food.

The Menu Groupings method places together all the non-perishable ingredients for your menu. Chili ingredients grouped together suggest that the canned tomatoes, the chili seasoning packet, and the chili beans are stored next to each other. The perishable chili meat would have to be kept in the refrigerator.

Continue organizing by storing all the day's menus together if you have space available in your cabinets. Wrap food in a grocery sack and store all the ingredients for a meal together. All the non-perishables for Monday's menus can be stored on one section of a shelf. Repeat the grouping of food for each day's menus Sunday through Saturday.

Consider grouping perishable items together in the refrigerator or freezer by Product or Menus. Under Product, all the beef or fruits or cheese would be stored close to each other. Under Menus, all the ingredients for one meal would be stored close to each other. Mark it--*Save, Do Not Eat*. Rewrap and freeze perishable foods that are for later menus. Label all frozen food by contents and date frozen.

If you store large quantities of food, write the month and year of purchase (example 7/03 for July, 2003) on the can or package. Store the new cans and packages at the back and rotate the older food forward on the shelves. A master inventory list of foods on the shelves and in the freezer is handy when you store large quantities of food. Unless you really buy in bulk and have large food storage, an inventory is not worth the time it takes to maintain.

A super organizer might attempt to keep a master inventory list of the food on the shelves. A master list requires keeping a list of everything you now have on your shelves, deleting an item when it is used, adding new items when they are purchased and keeping the list updated. Wow! A major project. But for the majority of meal planners, organize your shelves according to Product or Meal categories and that will be sufficient to help you keep track of what is available in your personal food store.

Food Preparation

Only Minutes until Dinner Time

Food preparation includes cooking or baking the food, serving the food, and cleaning up when the meal is over. This is number five and the last part of the food chain as explained in the book. Have you failed at meal planning before? Did you try to start with this part and ignored the other four parts that come before? When you do that, getting food ready is difficult. Follow the other steps *(Recipes, Planning, Buying, and Storage)* and *Food Preparation* is a snap.

Some people seem to prepare food with little effort. Others use up all their counter space plus end up with stacks of dirty dishes and trash. It always helps to clean the kitchen as you prepare food, but if that doesn't suit your schedule try to keep a little working space open and stack the dirty dishes in another area. Automatic dishwashers are perfect as a "get it out of the way" space for dirty dishes.

Now the time has come. You have planned your meals and you want to prove that you can get a meal on the table. The list below will give you a starting point. This is a handy sequence of events for meal preparation. Change the numbers to fit in with your own kitchen routine and stick with it until it becomes second nature and the chores on the list become a habit. After a few weeks of following this cycle of meal preparation as outlined below, you will be a pro at getting a meal on the table.

Delegation is a wonderful tool in preparing food since there are so many elements to each meal. Chose someone to set the table, another to do the dishes, and someone else to sweep the floor and take out the trash. Take turns cooking meals with family members preparing all or part of meals during the week. Use your calendar to assign these chores so there is no mistake about who has the chores tonight.

Let family members plan their meals using the Menu Planning Lists and make sure all the grocery ingredients are on the list before supermarket shopping day.

CHECKLIST FOR MEAL PREPARATION

1. Schedule time to fix your meal. (Major meal preparation and clean up takes at least an hour.)
2. Defrost frozen foods
3. Assemble foods to be made ahead of time. (Gelatin, yeast breads, marinated meat, potatoes boiled for salad, foods to be chilled, etc.)
4. Set table or prepare eating area
5. Take out all the ingredients to fix your meal. This is easy since your ingredients are pre-listed on your menu list and pre-purchased using your grocery list.
6. Prepare food. Just follow the recipes.
7. Serve food.
8. Enjoy eating your meal.
9. Clear table or eating area.
10. First, put things back in refrigerator
11. Second, put items back in cupboards
12. Third, throw trash in receptacle
13. Fourth, clear dishes
14. Package and store leftover food
15. Wash dishes. Scrub pots and pans. Dry by hand or in dishwasher. Put away.
16. Wipe off counter tops, stove and preparation areas
17. Sweep or mop kitchen floor.
18. Take out trash
19. Make any preparations for next meal. You may want to do this after you wash the dishes and before you clean the kitchen.
20. Dovetail your preparation so you cook for more than one meal at a time

Final Advice (If You Still Need a Little More Help)

Perhaps you completed all the steps in the food section of the book and you are still having trouble remembering what to fix for breakfast, lunch or dinner. Some people have trouble with the concept of writing down each menu onto the squares on the Menu Planner. I'll share an alternate method of simple menu planning for those people.

1. Buy a pad of small (approximately 1 1/2" x 2") sticky note paper.
2. Record on the sticky paper your menu for each meal. One paper might say "Steak, baked potatoes, green salad." Another might be "Pancakes, ham, orange juice."
3. Next buy a kitchen calendar. A magnetic "cook's calendar" with small spaces (about 2") for each day is handy to keep on the refrigerator.
4. Stick the papers on your calendar showing what you will have for Sunday or Tuesday or Whatever day's meals. Layer the papers, one--two--or three per day to plan Breakfast, Lunch and Dinner or a snack.
5. Prepare your meals according to your plan.
6. When things get out of hand and it becomes impossible to fix the Tuesday meals on Tuesday, switch with other meals during that week by moving the papers to another day on the calendar. So your Tuesday dinner might become Thursday's dinner. And the quick to fix Thursday dinner gets moved to Tuesday.

You should have all the ingredients for any meal since the meals were planned and the food was purchased during your weekly grocery shopping trip.

Keep this calendar in your kitchen on the refrigerator or cookbook stand or hung on the wall. Refer to it often.

Alternative--Instead of putting the sticky paper on a weekly kitchen calendar, you may keep track of the menus in your personal planning calendar. Switch meals just as you would on the weekly kitchen calendar by moving the papers from day to day. This added step should help you keep your menus in order and make it easier to switch meals according to convenience and time requirements.

That's all. Now you have each ingredient needed for successful menu planning. Start minimally and, ease into harder recipes and meals as you gain confidence and scale back when you are sick or your time schedule becomes too full. From now on, you have the tools to plan and prepare meals your way.

IT'S A FEAST!—Special Event Meal Planner

This Meal Planning List is for large dinners (Holidays, Thanksgiving, and Birthdays) when large quantities of food are served. The list gives you room to plan 3 Appetizers, 2 Appetizer Beverages, 5 Entrees, 3 Salads, 10 Side Dishes (Fruits, Vegetables, and Breads), 2 Meal Beverages, 3 Desserts, and 2 Dessert Beverages.

BEFORE THE MEAL FOOD ---

APPETIZER	APPETIZER	APPETIZER	BEVERAGE	BEVERAGE
LIST MAIN INGREDIENTS IN SPACES BELOW AND TRANSFER TO WEEKLY GROCERY LIST				

THE MAIN MEAL

ENTREE	ENTREE	ENTREE	ENTREE	ENTREE
LIST MAIN INGREDIENTS IN SPACES BELOW AND TRANSFER TO WEEKLY GROCERY LIST				

SALADS AND SIDE DISHES

SALAD	SALAD	SALAD	SIDE DISH	SIDE DISH
LIST MAIN INGREDIENTS IN SPACES BELOW AND TRANSFER TO WEEKLY GROCERY LIST				

SIDE DISHES

SIDE DISH	SIDE DISH	SIDE DISH	SIDE DISH	SIDE DISH
LIST MAIN INGREDIENTS IN SPACES BELOW AND TRANSFER TO WEEKLY GROCERY LIST				

SIDE DISHES AND MEAL BEVERAGES

SIDE DISH	SIDE DISH	SIDE DISH	BEVERAGE	BEVERAGE
LIST MAIN INGREDIENTS IN SPACES BELOW AND TRANSFER TO WEEKLY GROCERY LIST				

DESSERTS AND DESSERT BEVERAGES

DESSERT	DESSERT	DESSERT	BEVERAGE	BEVERAGE
LIST MAIN INGREDIENTS IN SPACES BELOW AND TRANSFER TO WEEKLY GROCERY LIST				

- Plan your large meal on the IT'S A FEAST! LIST. Use as many squares as you need for your special meal. The name of the dish is listed horizontally under the headings, one per square. (Example: Roasted Turkey) The ingredients needed for the dish are listed vertically under the MAIN INGREDIENT heading, under the name of the dish. Use extra spaces if needed.
- If menu items have been delegated to other participants put their name and dish they are bringing in the square. Then nothing is forgotten.
- Also, since you will need many serving bowls, plates, spoons and forks, make a notation by each dish which bowl or spoon you will need to serve the item.
- Transfer the main ingredients from this list to your **Weekly Grocery List** and never be short on food for your holiday meal.

FINANCIAL-MONEY MANAGEMENT

Need help getting control of your finances? I've tried many budget books and I finally made up my own. As a former bookkeeper, I came up with lists that are for the average wage earner. Software programs were too complex for me to use everyday and I went back to my handy, paper method. Choose the lists that seem simple and workable to you.

Money Management Section Includes These Lists:

INCOME AND TAXES

BUDGET AND ACTUAL EXPENSES

BUDGET AND EXPENSES FOR 2 PAYDAYS PER MONTH

BUDGET AND EXPENSES ALPHABETIZED

BUDGET AND EXPENSES, 2 PAYDAYS A MONTH, ALPHA

DAILY CREDIT CARD REGISTER

CREDIT CARDS AT A GLANCE

- Budget and Actual Expenses is a basic list of monthly expenses
- Budget # 2 is for those who are paid twice a month and want a specialized list. The first two budgets have items with the most important items near the top.
- Budget and Expenses Alphabetized has the information alphabetized
- Budget and Expenses Alpha # 2 is alphabetized for two paydays per month

List Organizer publishes a Budget Organizer for those people who want a simple, fill-in-the blank yearly money organizer

Begin by summarizing how much you make each month using the chart on the next page. To complete one of the lines on the page (Monthly expenses) you will need fill in one of the Budget pages and determine your outgoing money.

INCOME AND TAXES

January, February, March, April, May, June, July, August, September, October, November, December

WEEK	GROSS SALARY	OTHER INCOME	TAXES				NET INCOME
			FEDERAL (-)	STATE (-)or- Other Deductions	SOCIAL SECURITY (-)	MEDICARE (-)	(=)
1	$						
2	$						
3	$						
4	$						
5	$						
TOTAL➡	$	$	$	$	$	$	$

Cash Balance for Month

Cash on Hand	$
Salaried Net Income (Transfer from above or estimate)	(+)
Tips	(+)
Other Income (Child support, alimony, rents, dividends, royalties)	(+)
TOTAL ➡	(=) $
Subtract total monthly expenses (Get # by using one of the Budget lists)	(-)
This is your **Balance** or what you have left over. ➡	(=) $

BUDGET AND ACTUAL EXPENSES

MONTH OF:		ESTIMATED INCOME ➡			$
	BUDGET AMT	ACTUAL AMT	DIFFERENCE		
1. Housing (Mortgage / Rent)					
2. Electric / Gas					
3. Water					
4. Insurance, Car					
5. Insurance, Health					
6. Insurance, Life					
7. Credit card payments					
8. Installment loans					
9. Food					
10 Clothing					
11. Household expenses					
12. Telephone					
13. Cell telephone					
14. Trash collection					
15. Health, Doctor, Dentist					
16. Car payment					
17. Fuel and car expenses					
18. Contributions / Charity					
19. Savings					
20. Child care					
21. Education					
22. Entertainment / Recreation					
23. Gifts					
24. Personal					
25. Miscellaneous					
26. Taxes					
27. Repairs (Car, House, Etc.)					
28. Cable company					
29. Newspapers/ Magazines/ Books					
		ESTIMATED EXCESS ➡			$

If you have a plus sign in that last column, last row, you have stayed within your budget. If you have a minus sign and have gone in the red, you will be short on money this month. Solutions: Cut spending; Earn more money; Take out a loan.

BUDGET AND EXPENSES FOR 2 PAYDAYS PER MONTH

TO BE PAID	PAYCHECK #1 ESTIMATE	PAYCHECK #1 ACTUAL	PAYCHECK #2 ESTIMATE	PAYCHECK #2 ACTUAL	☑	TOTAL FOR MONTH
1. Housing (Mortgage / Rent)						
2, Electric / Gas						
3. Water						
4. Insurance, Car						
5. Insurance, Health						
6. Insurance, Life						
7. Credit Card Payments						
Discover or _____ Card						
MasterCard or _____ Card						
VISA or						
American Express or _____						
8. Installment loans						
9. Food						
10. Clothing						
11. Household expenses						
12. Telephone						
13. Cell telephone						
14. Trash collection						
15. Health, Doctor, Dentist						
16. Car payment						
17. Fuel and car expenses						
18. Contributions / Charity						
19. Savings						
20. Child care						
21. Education						
22. Entertainment / Recreation						
23. Gifts						

TO BE PAID	PAYCHECK #1 ESTIMATE	PAYCHECK #1 ACTUAL	PAYCHECK #2 ESTIMATE	PAYCHECK #2 ACTUAL	☑	TOTAL FOR MONTH
24. Personal						
25. Miscellaneous						
26. Taxes						
27. Repairs (Car, House, Etc.)						
28. Cable company						
29. Newspapers, magazines, books						
Estimated Income from this Paycheck						
Minus Estimate Expenses (From Above)						
Difference (plus or minus)						
Actual Gross from this Paycheck						
Actual Net from this Paycheck						
Minus Actual Expenses						
Cash on Hand or In the Red						

BUDGET AND EXPENSES ALPHABETIZED

MONTH OF		ESTIMATED INCOME ➡			$
	BUDGET AMT	**ACTUAL AMT**	**DIFFERENCE**		
1. Cable TV					
2. Car payment					
3. Cell telephone					
4. Child care					
5. Clothing					
6. Contributions / Charity					
7. Credit card payments					
American Express card or					
Discover card or					
Master Card or					
VISA card or					
8. Education					
9. Electric / Gas					
10 Entertainment / Recreation					
11 Food					
12. Fuel and car Expenses					
13. Gifts					
14. Health, Doctor, Dentist					
15. Household Expenses					
16. Housing (Mortgage / Rent)					
17. Installment Loans					
18. Insurance, Car					
19. Insurance, Health					
20. Insurance, Life					
21. Miscellaneous					

MONTH OF		ESTIMATED INCOME ➡		$
	BUDGET AMT	ACTUAL AMT	DIFFERENCE	
22. Newspapers, magazines, books				
23. Personal				
24. Repairs (Car, House, etc.)				
25. Savings				
26. Taxes				
27. Telephone				
28. Trash Collection				
29. Water				
		ESTIMATED EXCESS ➡		$

Month of _____

BUDGET AND EXPENSES, 2 PAYDAYS A MONTH, ALPHA

TO BE PAID	PAYCHECK #1 ESTIMATE	PAYCHECK #1 ACTUAL	PAYCHECK #2 ESTIMATE	PAYCHECK #2 ACTUAL	☑	TOTAL FOR MONTH
1. Cable TV						
2. Car payment						
3, Cell telephone						
4. Child care						
5. Clothing						
6. Contributions / Charity						
7. Credit Card Payments						
American Express or _____						
Discover or _____						
Master Card or						
VISA or _____						
8. Education						
9. Electric / Gas						
10. Entertainment / Recreation						
11. Food						
12. Fuel and car Expenses						
13. Gifts						
14. Health, Doctor, Dentist						
15. Household Expenses						
16. Housing (Mortgage / Rent)						
17. Installment loans						
18. Insurance, Car						
19. Insurance, Health						
20. Insurance, Life						
21. Miscellaneous						

TO BE PAID	PAYCHECK #1 ESTIMATE	PAYCHECK #1 ACTUAL	PAYCHECK #2 ESTIMATE	PAYCHECK #2 ACTUAL	☑	TOTAL FOR MONTH
22. Personal						
23. Repairs (Car, House, etc.)						
24. Savings						
25. Taxes						
26. Telephone						
27. Trash collection						
28. Water						
Estimated Income from this Paycheck						
Minus Estimate Expenses (From Above)						
Difference (plus or minus)						
Actual Gross from this Paycheck						
Actual Net from this Paycheck						
Minus Actual Expenses						
Cash on Hand or In the Red						

There are 2 styles of lists to keep track of your credit card debt. Try them both and chose the one that makes sense for you and your lifestyle. Just use one of them to keep track of those credit card purchases

DAILY CREDIT CARD REGISTER

Month of _____ **Last 4 digits of card number** _____

Cut Off Date _____ **Percentage Rate** _____

Type of Card and Name of Issuer _____

DAY	CHARGES AND CASH ADVANCES TODAY	(+) TOTAL FROM YESTERDAY	(-)CREDITS	(=)TOTAL ON CARD THIS MONTH
1	$			
2				
3				
4				
5				
6				
7				
8				
9				
10				
11				
12				
13				
14				
15				
16				
17				
18				
19				
20				
21				
22				
23				

DAY	CHARGES AND CASH ADVANCES TODAY	(+) TOTAL FROM YESTERDAY	(-)CREDITS	(=)TOTAL ON CARD THIS MONTH
24				
25				
26				
27				
28				
29				
30				
31				
TOTAL				

Monthly Totals from other Credit Cards

	THIS MONTH CHARGES AND CASH ADVANCES	(+) CARRY OVER FROM LAST MONTH	(-) PAYMENTS	(=)
VISA				+
VISA				+
MCARD				+
MCARD				+
DISCOVER				+
AMERICAN EXPRESS				+
				+
			GRAND TOTAL ➡	=

CREDIT CARDS AT A GLANCE

Keep track of four credit cards for a month. During the month, add the amounts from your new charge statements to the total from your previous day total statements. At a glance you can tell how much you have outstanding on each credit card. This list is to give you a quick overview of your total credit card debt. **Month of** _____

Day	Card	Card	Card	Card	TOTAL FOR DAY
1					
2					
3					
4					
5					
6					
7					
8					
9					
10					
11					
12					
13					
14					
15					
16					
17					
18					
19					
20					
21					
22					
23					

Day	Card	Card	Card	Card	TOTAL FOR DAY
24					
25					
26					
27					
28					
29					
30					
31					
Totals					

For example: You designate Column 1 as VISA and Column 2 as Discover. In Column 1 keep track of all your charges on your VISA card for the month. In Column 2 you will keep track of all your charges for Discover Card. If you want to know how much you have total for the day, add the total in the far right hand column. At the end of the month you may add up the total at the bottom to see what you spent on that credit card. You do not need to fill in each column each day--only when you have the time to update the list.

CLOTHES

People with fashion sense have learned how to create fashion statements with their clothes. They show up in clean, mended, color-coordinated, season-coordinated clothes each day of their lives. They seem to have an eye for the line of clothing and they know what looks good on them. Some become fashion consultants because they examine other people and know if they need a drop waist or a no-dart look. The rest of us get by matching a top and bottom item of clothing and hope we look suitable enough to get through the day.

Clothing is a major part of everyone's life. You may not cook your food or clean your house or even take care of your taxes. The odds are that you do dress yourself and are responsible for having clean clothes in your closet. We all get dressed each day. It is incredible that most of us do it so haphazardly. Do you really have any idea what clothes are in your closet right now, or if they fit the body you have today, or if they are clean and unwrinkled? No? You need the **Clothing Inventory List.**

It is simple to use, but it takes some time to fill in all the blanks. It can make an instantaneous difference in your clothing choices. It is the foundation which helps you discover your favorite clothes, which clothes are bargain losers, what mix and matches with anything else in your closet, and which clothes are right for today's weather.

It cannot help you discover your best colors or what style looks best on you. That is a subjective judgment which you have to make. This list is a place to keep track of what is hanging in the closet and whether it's worth it to you to *keep* it hanging in your closet.

The **Clothing Coordination Lists** let you group your separate pieces of clothing into outfits that look perfect together. The lists make choosing an outfit in the morning an easy decision and cut down on your "get ready" time. The three lists work best when combined. The **Inventory List** is a directory of your clothes. The **Coordination Lists** are an organization index of clothes and accessories that are compatible. You may use one, two, or all three lists according to your desire.

The **Clothing Inventory List** is meant to be a permanent list and a changing list of what is kept in your closet. It is permanent since you will keep it in a binder or your storage folder and you will refer to it to plan your wardrobe each week. It will change since you will be adding and deleting outfits to the list as you buy and discard clothing.

The **Inventory List** is organized to help you categorize the accumulation of clothes you now own. Take the list into your closet and quickly classify each item. Making a Clothes Inventory takes effort and time. Use this List only if it will help you organize your clothes. Circle one of the headings at the top of the page. For example, list all of your slacks on a page or your blouses or your nightclothes. Description might include type of neckline, button or pullover, beads, pleated, plaid or anything that would distinguish that article from another.

Clothes Section Includes These Lists:

CLOTHING INVENTORY

HIGH-POWERED OUTFIT COORDINATOR

SIMPLE OUTFIT COORDINATOR

CLOTHES STORAGE

DEEP CLEAN THE CLOTHES CLOSETS

CLOTHES BUYING LIST

CLOTHING CARE

WHAT YOU NEED FOR A LAUNDRY ROOM

HOW TO DO THE LAUNDRY

FABRIC / SEWING PROJECT LIST

How to Fill Out Inventory List

To make a clothes inventory takes effort and time, perhaps more time than you have--unless you tackle the job in phases. Start with one page of inventory and add pages as you have time. Each page is easy to complete.

Y The first grouping of clothes is according to type): "Blouses, Shirts" "Slacks, Pants, Jeans, Shorts" "Skirts, Dresses" "Suits, Blazers" "Sweaters, Vests" "Coats, Jackets" "Shoes, Boots" "Swimsuits" "Nightclothes" "Underwear" Circle one of these headings at the top of your page to indicate which grouping of clothing is inventoried on the page.

Y The second grouping of clothes is according to season:
Spring/Summer/Autumn/Winter. Decide what time of the year you would wear the apparel.
Circle one or two of the seasons to indicate your preference. Some of you may live where you wear the same clothes year around and you would not bother with this grouping.

Y The third grouping of clothes is a description of the article of clothing.

Y The fourth grouping of clothes is according to color: *Red, Blue, Yellow, Purple, Green, Orange, Pink, White, Black, Grey or Brown.*

Categorize the clothes according to the major color in the item. Do not worry too much about the exact color. You will determine the shades and tints of the colors later. Classify the shirt as Red whether it is red-orange or bluish-red. When you make out your Coordination Lists you can narrow down the colors to what red garment matches another red garment.

Y The fifth grouping is by size. This helps you determine if the clothing article fits you or--maybe it's history because of weight gain or loss.
Use pencil to fill out the list since you may be throwing out tops or pants as you change your mind about their worth.

It's Simple

1. Circle the Type and Season at the top of the page.
2. Provide a brief description of all garments of one type and season. (Column 1)
3. Specify the garment's color. (Column 2)
4. Specify the garment's style (Column 3)
5. Specify the garment's fabric (Column 4)
6. As time permits, try on each garment and indicate if it fits. You may want to specify size if your closet has clothes of more than one size. (Column 5)
7. Repeat steps 1 through 6 until your Clothes Inventory is complete.

You will refer to the list when buying new clothes, discarding old clothes, deciding what to wear, and combining outfits.
Example: All spring/ summer short-sleeved shirts might be listed on one page. Description might include type of neckline, button or pullover, beaded, pleated, plaid, brand name, or anything that would distinguish that article of clothing from another.

LISTS FOR MUDDLE MANAGEMENT

CLOTHING INVENTORY

Type of clothing on this page (Circle One): **"Blouses, Shirts"**   **"Slacks, Pants, Jeans, Shorts"**   **"Skirts, Dresses"**   **"Suits, Blazers"** **"Sweaters, Vests"** **"Coats, Jackets"**   **"Shoes, Boots"**   **"Swimsuits"** **"Nightclothes"**   **"Underwear"**

SEASON: Spring/ Summer/ Autumn/ Winter

Describe clothing according to Style, Brand, Fabric, Sleeve length, Decoration, Design or anything that will help you remember what piece of clothing you are describing.

Description of Clothing	Color	Style	Fabric	Size

How To Use the Coordination Lists

The **Clothes Coordination Lists** are coordination tools to be used with your **Clothes Inventory List**. The Inventory List describes separate articles of clothing. The Coordination Lists coordinate those clothes to make outfits. Never again will you rush through the house trying to match clothes. You only have to refer to your Coordination Lists and choose an appropriate outfit for the occasion. Also, the lists will jog your memory to help you recall what is clean and ready to wear and what fits.

The # 1 Coordination List is for outfits that include jewelry, shoes, belts, coats and clothing. I call it the High-Powered Outfit Coordinator for people who want to look extra sharp.

HIGH-POWERED OUTFIT COORDINATOR (Sample)

#_____ or Name of Outfit_____

Top Piece Clothing	Bottom Piece Clothing	Sweater / Blazer / Vest	Shoe / Sock / Nylon
Black wool shell, med.	Black/print skirt (wool) Size 10	Dark green wool blazer	Black heels, bow front ,leather
Coat	**Underwear**	**Jewelry / Scarf / Belt /**	**Handbag / Hat**
Black wool	Black half slip Black bra	Green & gold necklace Gold hoop earrings	Black leather

The # 2 Coordination List is for simple outfits that include only a top and bottom piece of clothing with a sweater or vest or accessory. Most of us will use this List.

SIMPLE OUTFIT COORDINATOR (Sample)

Top Piece of Clothing	Bottom Piece of Clothing	Accessory (Shoe, Jewelry, Blazer)
1. Pink T-shirt/long sleeve	Dark pink denim	Navy V-neck Sweater
2. Turq. Turtle neck	Frosted light jeans	Turquoise Blazer / Brown loafers

Identify your clothes according to Style, Brand Fabric, Sleeve length, Hem Length, Decoration, Design, or anything that help you quickly identify which piece of clothing you want to coordinate.

You may subdivide each page into clothes for different occasions:

- Casual/Home Attire
- School/Office Attire
- Dress Attire
- Formal/Party Attire
- Sports/Play Attire

Circle one of these labels at the top of the page to specify what type of attire will be listed on the page. Types of attire should be grouped together on a page. Sub-label each page according to season. The top of your list would be divided into a type of attire (example: casual) and a season (spring/summer). Subdivide ensembles using as many pages, types of attire, and seasons as you like.

Clothing coordination is similar to menu coordination. You need to determine what separate items go together for a nice appearance. Instead of food recipes, you plan clothing apparel that enhances your image. The wonderful part is if you make a mistake and it does not work, you can delete the piece of clothing from your Coordination List and keep changing the garments until you coordinate outfits that look good on you and make you feel good about yourself. The Coordination Lists become valuable with their lists of your favorite outfits.

It will be apparent that some of the clothes hanging in your clothes do not seem to coordinate with anything else and they might as well be shipped out to the consignment or thrift store, or you need to add coordinating garments to match with the ugly duckling left outs. The List will help you evaluate your wardrobe and show you alternatives to your usual wardrobe coordination. You will add variety to what you now own. This Coordination Lists will be changing as you change your mind or add or discard clothing.

The working person should start out with one page of five office outfits for one week. The at home worker needs to coordinate five home outfits. Almost everyone needs a page to list more formal costumes, even if they are only used once or twice a year.

Do not be surprised if you find you need page after page to match up all of your apparel. At first do not try to synchronize everything in your closet unless you have hours to spend on that project or you do not own many clothes. As you wear outfits you like, add these new ensembles to your lists.

Each person will use the list differently. Some may glance at the list each day to decide what to wear. The really organized will plan ahead and write down on their calendar what they are going to wear each day during the coming week or month. Always make sure what you plan to wear is clean or your coordinating outfit will be missing an important part.

Add to the Coordination Lists as you wear outfits that you love. Erase or cross off apparel that you hated when you actually wore them together. These lists are guides to help you plan in a hurry. Guides help steer you in the right direction, but you can still change your mind.

HIGH-POWERED OUTFIT COORDINATOR

#_____ or Name of Outfit_____

Top Piece Clothing	Bottom Piece Clothing	Sweater / Blazer / Vest	Shoe / Sock / Nylon
Coat	**Underwear**	**Jewelry / Scarf / Belt**	**Handbag / Hat**

#_____ or Name of Outfit_____

Top Piece Clothing	Bottom Piece Clothing	Sweater / Blazer / Vest	Shoe / Sock / Nylon
Coat	**Underwear**	**Jewelry / Scarf / Belt**	**Handbag / Hat**

#_____ or Name of Outfit_____

Top Piece Clothing	Bottom Piece Clothing	Sweater / Blazer / Vest	Shoe / Sock / Nylon
Coat	**Underwear**	**Jewelry / Scarf / Belt**	**Handbag / Hat**

#_____ or Name of Outfit_____

Top Piece Clothing	Bottom Piece Clothing	Sweater / Blazer / Vest	Shoe / Sock / Nylon
Coat	Underwear	Jewelry / Scarf / Belt	Handbag / Hat

#_____ or Name of Outfit_____

Top Piece Clothing	Bottom Piece Clothing	Sweater / Blazer / Vest	Shoe / Sock / Nylon
Coat	Underwear	Jewelry / Scarf / Belt	Handbag / Hat

#_____ or Name of Outfit_____

Top Piece Clothing	Bottom Piece Clothing	Sweater / Blazer / Vest	Shoe / Sock / Nylon
Coat	Underwear	Jewelry / Scarf / Belt	Handbag / Hat

SIMPLE OUTFIT COORDINATOR

Top Piece of Clothing	Bottom Piece of Clothing	Accessory (Shoe, Jewelry, Blazer)

Clothes Storage

The old way to plan a closet is to get a rod, secure it in the closet and put some hangers on the rod. The new way to plan a closet--measure your space; decide if the rods will be for long or short clothes; add shelving, drawers, specialized organizers, and various types of hangers.

Closets have changed. Sometimes they are as large as bedrooms used to be. Clever people have manufactured many closet organizers including shelves, drawers, and racks to help make the closet an organized area. Consultants will help you plan closet space. Most large decorator and hardware stores carry pre-packaged closet organizers with instructions for self-installation. Closets have become fun and user-friendly.

Closet organization is not a new trend. Mail order catalogues have been selling plastic hanging shoe or sweater racks for years along with stacking cardboard boxes. These handy gadgets take up space. You have to plan your closet so you do not end up with plenty of organizing gadgets and not enough space for your clothes.

1. Measure your closet. By using your Clothes Inventory List you can tell quickly if you need room for blouses or shirts that take up less vertical hanging space or if you have dresses and pants, which need a longer area for hanging. Shoe storage needs can be determined by the number of shoes and boots you own. Your Clothes Inventory can help you plan your closet by reminding you what you own.

2. How many rods do you need for hanging clothes?

Estimate how much space you need for your clothes. Measure how much space each category of clothing now takes on a rod in your closet.
Rod for shirts, blouses: How many inches long?
Rod for dresses, pants, coats: How many inches long?
Rod for skirts, suits: How many inches long?

3. Hangers are still a necessity. How many do you need?

    Wooden hangers for coats and suits: #
    Pants hangers: #
    Skirt hangers: #
    Padded hangers: #
    Plastic tube hangers: #
    Wire hangers: #
4. Clothing storage units: How many do you need?

    Shoe rack: #
    Stacking box: #
    Tie rack: #
    Belt rack: #
    Sweater shelf: #
    Handbag and hat shelf: #

Plan your closet organizing needs by using the information you listed above. Make a sketch of your closet and make a list of the materials you need to store your clothes.

You may find you have too many clothes for your closet. Discard the extra clothes, find space in boxes under the bed, or move them to an extra closet. Do not crowd your closet. Do not store dirty clothing in your closets. Clean clothes before storing them in closets or drawers. After taking off clothes each day, air them out before putting them away in the closet.

Organize Closets by Category

Most stores group their clothing displays according to categories to make it easier for the customer to find what they need. You need to do the same in your closet where you are the regular patron. The most common groupings for clothes are the same as were used in your Clothes Inventory List

- By season, (autumn/winter or spring/summer)
- By type (shirt, pants, sweater, shoe, etc.)
- By color.
- By ensembles

Long-sleeved blue blouses may be kept by other long-sleeved blue blouses. That trick will save you minutes each day since clothes put away by category are easy to find when you are rushed.

Also you are able to find clothes easily when you use your Clothes Coordination Lists. You won't be searching for your red print skirt at the last minute. Your blue suit will be easy to find next to your other suits. When you put away clothes each day or after laundering, hang them according to categories and your closet will take shape in a hurry.

Clothes in Drawers

Clothes may also be stored on shelves or in drawers. Folded clothes shut in drawers need to be clean so the dirt and odors don't stay trapped in a closed chest of drawers. Line drawers with shelf paper (scented or regular). Add sachets or cedar balls. Instead of folding clothes, you may wish to roll them to prevent creases.

Subdivide drawers using drawer dividers, shoe boxes, or plastic zipper dividers. Inexpensive dividers can be made from cut up cardboard boxes.

DEEP CLEAN THE CLOTHES CLOSETS

To clean my clothes closets and drawers I need to:	Closet #1	Closet #2	Closet #3
Measure my closet: the rod (vertical and horizontal space)			
Measure space for shoes			
Measure shelf space in closet			
Measure drawer space in closet			
Take measurements and rethink closet space--how much space for tops, skirts, pants, suits, dresses, shoes, sweaters, etc.			
Plan how many articles of clothing you need to throw out or put into storage so you can fit your clothes into available closet space			
Sketch closet design			
Rethink the organization of the closet. You will group by seasonal clothes, type of clothes (blouses, pants, etc.), color of clothes, or planned outfits.			
Buy new hangers (Wooden, pants, skirt, padded, coordinated plastic tube, wire, etc. according to the number of clothes)			
Buy new storage items--Plastic shoe boxes or shoe racks			
Stacking boxes			
Shelves or drawers			
Tie and belt holders			
Hooks for handbags, hat, coats, etc.			
Now you can start to go through the clothes--Try on clothes if needed. Set up Five Areas			
#1 Keep this item. It's clean and it fits.			
#2 Keep this item. It needs to be dry cleaned, washed, altered.			
#3 Discard this item. It's good enough to go to thrift store.			
#4 Discard this item. Take to consignment store/ keep for sale.			
#5 Discard this item. It goes into the trash.			
Clean the rods, shelves, vacuum floors, etc.			
Hang up the #1 pile on good hangers, organized by group following your plan and design for this closet.			
Hang up the clothes for this current season			
Group clothes together by color--light colors to			

To clean my clothes closets and drawers I need to:	Closet #1	Closet #2	Closet #3
dark colors			
Group similar items tops, bottoms, nightclothes, etc.			
Face clothes in one direction			
Put in trash bags and throw out the #5 pile			
Put the #4 pile into bags, take to consignment store			
Put the #3 pile into boxes, bags and drop off at thrift store			
Put the #2 pile into three smaller piles--take one to the dry cleaner, one to the tailor for alterations, and wash the remaining pile			
Repeat this process for the clothes in your drawers, armoires, etc.			
Go through your shoes using the same piles.			
Polish shoes. Take for repair			
Move out-of-season clothes to storage closet or box--cover			
Line drawers with shelf /lingerie paper. Add sachets or cedar balls			
Subdivide drawers using drawer dividers. Make your own out of cut up pieces of cardboard.			
Put back underwear, socks, nylons, etc. in drawers			
Clean out handbags, wallets			
Polish and repair handbags, belts, wallets, etc.			
Use the Clothes Inventory List to keep track of your clothes			
Use the Coordination Lists to pre-plan clothes			
Use the Buying List to plan your clothes purchases.			

PAGE #_____

CLOTHES BUYING LIST

This list helps you plan what clothes you need to buy to supplement your wardrobe. After you buy the article, add it to your Clothes Inventory List, if you use that List, and coordinate into outfits on your Coordination Lists.

I Need to Buy: (Description)	Coordinates With? Other Clothes	Estimated Price $	☑ Purchased

Clothing Care

Once there was a girl named Alicia who employed a maid to take care of all her clothing needs. When she was a young adult, Alicia went away to college and shared an apartment with other girls who had not grown up with maids. Soon it became apparent that her roommates knew how to take care of their clothes, and she, not wanting to appear inept and having no training in laundering methods, devised her own clothing organization system. Alicia threw her dirty clothes under her bed and bought new clothes to hang in her closet. This worked until the legs of her bed lifted off the ground because there were so many dirty clothes underneath the box springs.

Her dorm mother said, "Clean out these clothes from under your bed! It's a mess." So, being resourceful once more, Alicia bought large garbage bags and filled them with all the clothes under the bed and put them out for the garbage man to take. In her estimation she had solved the problem. Her room was clean and she had room for more clothes.

What a sight Alicia missed when all the girls from her dormitory who wore the same size as she did, rummaged through the garbage bags, grabbing her discarded clothing. They were willing to launder or dry clean the seldom worn clothes. (Based on a true story.)

Now Alicia had something most of us do not have--a rich father. Most of us need to learn how to clean and mend our clothes.

Today individual pieces of clothing are marked with care instructions. Before you buy a blouse you can tell if it has to be dry cleaned or hand washed or ironed. The neophyte laundry care person who uses a Laundromat may want to simplify life by buying clothes that say "Machine Wash, Tumble Dry". Most of us understand how to put quarters into a coin-operated washing machine and clothes dryer that handle easy care clothes.

Clothes of natural fibers are popular. While they are easy to clean, they need to be ironed. Some silks need to be dry-cleaned while others may be washed. You have to live with the clothes you have chosen, but as you replace them, you might want to buy easier care clothing or calendar your time to give special care fabrics the cleaning they require.

Let's make doing the laundry easy. Since clothes are getting dirty even while you are washing the ones from yesterday, laundry goes on and on. The **Laundry Room List** helps you set up a laundry room or area with the correct cleaning equipment. You don't need everything that is listed here. Pick and choose what you want in your laundry basket. Then the next list-- How to do the Laundry--tells you, surprise, how to do the laundry in case you don't have a clue how to start.

WHAT YOU NEED FOR A LAUNDRY ROOM

Pick and Choose and what do you need in your Laundry room

➡ Bags for dirty clothes	➡ Hydrogen peroxide--blood stains
➡ Bags, zippered, for small items and lingerie	➡ Iron
➡ Bleach, all fabric	➡ Ironing board and pad
➡ Bleach, chlorine	➡ Presoak laundry booster
➡ Bluing	➡ Safety pins
➡ Bottle, spray	➡ Sewing kit (See Sewing Kit List)
➡ Brush, clothes	➡ Sizing, fabric
➡ Brush, lint remover	➡ Soap, laundry (Fels-Naptha, Boraxo)
➡ Brush, scrub	➡ Soap flakes, mild soap (Ivory flakes, Woolite)
➡ Cloth, pressing	➡ Stain removers
➡ Clothes dryer	➡ Starch (liquid or spray)
➡ Clothes line or drying rack	➡ Static spray
➡ Clothes pins and bag	➡ Thread (snag) puller for knit fabrics
➡ Cups for measuring detergent or bleach	➡ Washing machine
➡ Detergent, laundry	➡
➡ Dry cleaning home kit	➡
➡ Fabric softener (liquid or sheets)	➡
➡ Hampers for clothes	➡

HOW TO DO THE LAUNDRY

Have you ever wanted someone to give you a list telling you how to do the laundry? You have found that list. It's not fancy or complicated. It's some straight forward advice that might keep you from turning a load of laundry the wrong color. While we are talking about that--never put reds of bright pinks in the same load with anything else. Even if you wash them with dark jeans, you may end up with your white jean pockets turning pink. Yes, I speak from experience. Also, I will tell you not to wash dark blue jeans and towels with anything but dark blues. Again, it's experience talking.

1. **SORT**--Divide into Light colored fabrics and Dark colored fabrics in the following fabric types.

    A. Hand washables (Lights and Darks separate)

    B. Machine washables (Lights and Darks separate)

    C. Dry clean only fabrics

    D. Delicate fabrics (Lights and Darks separate)

    E. Permanent press fabrics (Lights and Darks separate)

    F. Heavily soiled clothing (Lights and Darks separate)

    G. Towels (Light and Darks separate)

2. **PREPARE CLOTHES FOR WASHING**

    A. Turn delicate fabric items, heavily soiled clothes or clothes with special buttons, inside out.

    B. Zip zippers and turn large zippered items inside out.

    C. Button buttons on special items and tie ribbons and drawstrings.

3. **PRESOAK OR PRESPOT**

    A. Spray or treat stains, collars, etc.

    B. Soak stained items in soapy water. Soak some stained items in water with bleach--careful with this.

    C. Scrub with brush or sponge

4. **MACHINE WASH**

   A. Add detergent or soap flakes

   B. Fill bleach or fabric softener dispenser

   C. Choose wash cycle, rinse cycle, speed, water temperature and water level. (Hot water is needed to activate some detergents. Cold water temperature washes need a special cold water detergent to clean the clothes.)

   D. Start water in cycle.

   E. Add clothes when detergent is dissolved. Do not pour detergent, bleach or fabric softener on top of clothes.

   F. When cycle is finished, remove clothes to clothes dryer, hangers or flat area depending on drying technique required.

   G. Wipe washer tub and top at end of wash day. Clean out filters.

5. **MACHINE DRY**

   A. Choose dryer cycle and temperature.

   B. Clean lint filter

   C. Add fabric softener sheet

   D. Add sorted clothes and start dryer.

6. **LINE DRY OR DRY FLAT**

   A. Use a clothes line or clothes rack, inside or outside, and hang clothes with clothespins.

   B. Reshape and flat dry special items. Use a non-wood surface, covered with an absorbent, white towel.

7. **HAND WASH**--Use this technique for special care items such as lingerie or silk fabrics

    A. Fill basin with warm or tepid water.

    B. Dissolve mild soap.

    C. Swish garments in suds.

    D. Squeeze out excess water. Do not twist.

    E. Drain water. Refill with clean water.

    F. Rinse in clean water.

    G. Squeeze out excess water. Do not twist.

    H. Hang to dry or dry flat as indicate.

8. **FOLD**--Sort according to individual's clothes
9. **IRON CLOTHES**
10. **PUT AWAY CLOTHES**
11. **TAKE SPECIAL CARE CLOTHES TO DRY CLEANERS**

Those are some of the basics. Feel free to add or delete your own preferences to make laundry day a clothes drying breeze. And, yes, you can Sort-Wash-Dry-Fold-Put Away as a real basic laundering technique.

Use the Fabric Project List to keep track of sewing projects that you've begun. Too often, we start quilts or dresses and never finish them because we don't have all the items or forget we started the project. Keep track of what sewing projects you started and when you started them and when you hope to finish them.

FABRIC / SEWING PROJECT LIST

DESCRIPTION OF PROJECT	NEED TO BUY	START DATE	FINISH DATE PROJECTED

Organize Desk and Paper Files Section Includes These Lists::

ORGANIZE THE WORKSPACE

ORGANIZE THE FILING SYSTEM

CATEGORIES FOR FILE FOLDERS

KEEP THESE PAPERS IN A SECURE PLACE

SORT AND PURGE PAPER FILES

HOW LONG TO KEEP PAPERS

ORGANIZE MAIL AND FAXES

ADDRESS BOOK PAGE

ORGANIZE THE WORK SPACE

Eliminate the clutter. Clean off the desk. Get it off the kitchen counter and into a box or desk. Whether you use the dining room table as a temporary desk or have a dedicated office, you will need some of these items.

Check items you want to add to each workspace in your home or office.	Desk #1	Desk #2	Desk #3
Address book / Telephone book			
Books (Reference & others) / Bookshelf			
Bulletin board			
Calendar (Planning book)			
Chair / Acrylic floor mat			
Clips (Binder and Paper clips)			
Clock			
Computer / monitor / keyboard / printer / scanner			
Diskettes / CDs			
Envelopes			
FAX machine			
File folders and accessories			
Greeting cards			
Highlighting pens			
Hole punch			
In and out baskets			
Label maker			
Lamp			
Letter opener			
Note pads / Legal pads			
Paper / Stationery / Postcards			
Pens / Pencils and Sharpener			
Push pins			

Check items you want to add to each workspace in your home or office.	Desk #1	Desk #2	Desk #3
Return address labels			
Rubber bands			
Ruler			
Scissors			
Stamps			
Stapler / Staple remover / Staples			
Tape (various sizes and types)			
Telephone / Answering machine			
Wastebaskets			
White board & eraser & markers			
Plus: Organizers of all types and sizes			

ORGANIZE THE FILING SYSTEM

To organize my filing system I need to:	Home	Home Office	Work Office
Rethink my system (Folders, Labels, Binders, File cabinet, Color-coding, Combining systems, etc.)			
Go to the File Category List and decide # of files needed			
Go to a store or look online at paper file organizing products			
Buy or make a filing box or cabinet			
Buy file folders (a combination of hanging, manila & expandable)			
Buy labels or labeling machine for file folders--or use labeling system on computer			
Buy colored dots or labels for color-coding categories. Or buy colored folders and group by type			
Buy binders for larger file categories			
Buy three-hole punch if using binders (Or two-hole punch if you are top punching papers)			
Buy a stapler for multiple pages (Do not file paper clipped items since the clips fall off. Or use binder clips)			
Set up a "To Be Filed" box, shelf or drawer (A folder is usually too small for all that goes inside.)			
Clear out old files and shred or toss old papers			
Use this List in conjunction with your Mail System			

CATEGORIES FOR FILE FOLDERS

Start with a few categories and add more as needed. Individualize your own system and chose the categories that make sense to you or make up your own file folder names. If someone helps you file, let them help you choose the categories.

•	1. Set up General Categories First ---- add Sub-Categories (in parenthesis) as needed
•	2. File alphabetically
•	3. Use expandable files or binders for large categories
•	4. Make labels easy to read (Print or use label maker)
•	5. If you have multiple file systems at home, try to combine them into one area
•	6. Compile a master list of the categories you chose and keep in the front of the files

Some Suggested Categories for File Folders	Home	Home Office	Work Office
Addresses / Birthdays / Anniversaries			
Automobile (Maintenance / Repairs / Insurance / Loan / Books)			
Beauty			
Certificates (Birth / Church / Death / Marriage)			
Charity (Receipts / Newsletters / Donation Record)			
Child care			
Children (Files for each child with sub-categories)			
Church (Donations / Ordinances / Addresses)			
Committee information			
Crafts (Needlework / Wood / Painting / Scrap booking / etc.)			
Education			
Employment			
Entertaining			
Entertainment / Recreation			
Estate Information (Wills / Living Will / Funeral Info / Power of Attorney / Medical / Insurance / Trust Info)			
Family History			
Financial (Budget / Credit card receipts / Credit cards / Stocks-Bonds-Mutual Funds / Bank Information / Stockbrokers/ Savings / Income / Capital Gains)			

Some Suggested Categories for File Folders	Home	Home Office	Work Office
Health / Exercise			
Hobbies (Personalized sub-categories)			
Holiday / Gifts			
Home maintenance			
Home ideas			
Household Inventory			
Humor / Cartoons			
Insurance (Auto--for each car / Life / Home / Medical)			
Investments			
Legal			
Maps			
Medical (Doctor / Dental / Vision / Prescriptions / Insurance / Claims to-be-submitted / Claims submitted)			
Memberships			
Nutrition / Diet			
Personal Information			
Pets			
Real Estate			
Recipes (with many sub-categories)			
Resume			
Retirement			
Safe Deposit Box (Contents / Bills) See Important Papers List			
Sports			
Stamps, postal			
Taxes (Deductions / Receipts / Real Estate Taxes / Mortgage / Charitable Donations / Business Expenses / & many more)			
Telephone (Cell / Regular / Long Distance)			
Travel Ideas			
Trusts			
Upcoming events (Invitations / Clippings)			
Utilities			
Warranties			

KEEP THESE PAPERS IN A SECURE PLACE

Very important: (Keep in safe deposit box or fireproof safe or box)	Important: (Keep in safe place in the house so others can find this information)
Adoption papers	Automobile registration, maintenance
Automobile titles (Include other titles for boats, trailers, etc.)	Bank statements with cancelled checks (3 years for personal)
Bank savings certificates and information	Copies of information that is in the safe-deposit box
Birth certificates	Credit card information, statements, etc.
Citizenship papers	Education information (diplomas, financial aid, correspondence)
Custody agreements	Employment history
Death certificates and papers	Home improvement information
Divorce decree and papers	Income statements, pay stubs
Estate planning documents	Insurance information, statements
Household inventory	Investment information, statements
Insurance policies	Loan information
Leases	Mortgage statements
Legal documents (contracts, bill of sales, court papers, etc.	Receipts for major purchases
Licenses	Retirement information
Marriage licenses	Social security information
Medical and immunization records	Tax receipts for itemized deductions
Military records	Tax returns along with all forms and receipts needed for audits
Mortgage and closing papers, titles	Warranties and service contracts
Passport	
Photos	
Pre-nuptial agreements	
Stock certificates	
Wills	

SORT AND PURGE PAPER FILES

To file papers in my filing system I need to:	Home	Home Office	Work Office
Set up a new system using the File Categories & Paper Files Lists			
Before starting, have some blank labels and folders available for new categories			
1. Take one paper at a time off the top of your To-File stack 2. Quickly decide where you want to file it (under which category) 3. Optional--In the top, right-hand corner of that paper, write the name of the category--important if many people use the file system 4. Drop it into the correct folder 5. Put newest items at the front, oldest at the back 6. File alphabetically 7. Some items need to be hole punched and put in binders--do it now 8. If you don't have a folder for that piece of paper, make one now & file it alphabetically in your system. 9. As you put new items into a folder, purge old documents you no longer need. Shred or tear up old papers. Recycle if you can. 10. Continue sorting and purging paper files until the pile is gone (or you need a quick break from this tedious task) 11. Don't give up. Keep at that pile until it is gone			
Schedule on your Monthly To-Do List that filing needs to be done--every month			

HOW LONG TO KEEP PAPERS

To purge papers in my filing system I need to know how long to keep them:

(This is NOT a legally correct list, check with your accountant or lawyer before destroying any of these papers.)

TYPE OF DOCUMENT	HOW LONG TO KEEP
Almost anything on the left side of the Important Papers List	Keep forever.
Things on the right side of the list	Keep as needed
Automobile titles & maintenance--	Until you sell the automobile
Automobile registration--	Until renewal & you get new registration
Bank ATM or deposit slips	Until reconciled with monthly statement
Bank statements & cancelled checks	Personal accounts, 3 years (7 if you have complex statements) Business accounts, 7 years (Forever if you file complex tax returns)
Bill statements	Until payments are credited or keep if needed for tax deductions
Brokerage statement	Until you discontinue account plus 3-7 years
Credit card information	Until you discontinue account plus 1 year
Credit card statements & receipts	1 year (helps with taxes & retail store returns)
Divorce documents	Forever
Estate documents	Forever
House legal papers	Keep while you own the house plus 5 years after sale
Income statements	Until reconciled with employer records at year's end (W-2s or 1099s in the United States)
Insurance policies	While they are in effect plus 3 years
Insurance statements	Until renewal or 1 year to compare rates
Investment information	7 years after sale to prove cost basis
Loan information	3 years after payoff
Medical bills	3 years
Medical insurance information	1 year after cancellation
Medical records	Forever (even after death the family

	may need these records)
Mortgage statements	Until reconciled with yearly summary
Receipts for major items	Keep while you own item for proof of purchase warranty
Retirement information	Forever, or until death of all recipients
Tax information for itemized deductions	Keep with tax returns 7 years (Such as W-2s, 1099s, charitable contributions, receipts, tax notices, medical deductions)
Tax returns & papers that prove return	7 years (If you have complex returns and you may be audited, keep returns forever)
Warranties & Instructions	Until you sell or dispose of the item

ORGANIZE MAIL AND FAXES

To organize my paper mail I need to:	Home	Home Office	Work Office
Rethink the flow of mail from box to desk to reply to file box			
Go to a store or look online at mail organizing products			
Buy or make an in box for mail (big enough for all mail)			
Put the in box in a convenient place so mail gets in there			
Purchase name & address labels			
Purchase greeting cards, thank you notes, postcards etc.			
Purchase envelopes, opener, stamps, sealer, paper, pens, etc.			
Optional: Purchase a paper shredder			
Purchase a large wastebasket and liners			
Purchase magazine files for periodicals			
Find a flat area (desk, table) where you can open mail			
Put supplies in a drawer nearby, OR			
Put supplies in a portable box if mail area is a shared area			
Purchase or make 5 file folders			
Label file folders #1 Bills to Pay #2 Save and File #3 Need Reply #4 Copy #5 Ready to Send (Outgoing Mail)			
Keep file folders in a file box close to desk or in portable box			
When you open mail: **Read, Sort** into file folders, **Shred** or throw out junk mail. (Shred junk mail with your name on applications)			
When all mail is open and sorted, go back through each folder and complete the necessary work as time permits.			
Pay the bills in folder #1			
File the mail in folder #2			
Reply to or take action on mail in folder #3			
Copy or scan the mail in folder #4			
Purchase postage and send mail in folder #5			

To organize my paper mail I need to:	Home	Home Office	Work Office
Pre-address greeting cards for the month & put them in folder #5			
The wastebasket becomes file folder #6. Fill it up with unwanted paper, coupons, catalogues, from the mail			
If you keep catalogues, put them on the shelf or into magazine files and throw out expired issues.			
Put periodicals into magazine files. Discard old issues			

For mailing organizers try Target, Wal-Mart, Staples, Office Max or your local office supply store. Online try www.organize-everything.com   www.organizeit.com www.containerstore.com   Prices vary according to materials.

ADDRESS BOOK PAGE

FIRST NAME	NICKNAME	**LAST NAME**
STREET ADDRESS	CITY, STATE	ZIP
HOME TELEPHONE	2ND TELEPHONE LINE	FAX
CELL TELEPHONE	PAGER	E-MAIL
BIRTHDAY	SPOUSE BIRTHDAY	ANNIVERSARY
SPOUSE NAME	CELL TELEPHONE	PAGER/E-MAIL
CHILDREN'S NAMES	ADDRESS	BIRTHDAY
YEAR CHRISTMAS CARD SENT	YEAR CARD RECEIVED	
GIFTS EXCHANGED		

WHAT I NEED TO TAKE

This section contains some of my favorite Lists that save me a great deal of frustration. When I leave the house, I need to fill the car with lots of odds and ends depending on my destination.   These fun lists say, "Take this along or you'll be sorry."

What to Take Section Includes These Lists

PLACES I NEED TO GO TODAY

WHAT TO TAKE TO WORK

WHAT TO TAKE ON A PICNIC

WHAT TO TAKE ON A HIKE

WHAT TO TAKE TO AN OUTDOOR CONCERT

The first List, **Places I Need to Go Today**, is wonderful when you have to make many stops and need to remember to take along items from home. It's a mind tickler

PLACES I NEED TO GO TODAY

Attorney's Office / Legal	<u>Library</u> (Books, Card, <u>Research Materials</u>)
<u>Auto</u> Shop	Music Store / Music Lessons / Dance Lessons
Bank or Credit Union (Cash / Checks signed / Deposit slips filled in / ATM or Debit Card / Papers / Items for Safe Deposit Box / Payments)	Office Supply Store
Barber Shop / Beauty Shop	Physician (Insurance papers / ID card / Payment, X-rays, Medical records)
Child Pre-school / Day Care	Post Office (Letters / Stamps / Return address labels / Envelopes / Packages / Mail Box key / Money)
Church	Restaurant
Dentist (Insurance papers/ ID card / Payment)	School
Department Store	Shopping Mall
Discount Store	Specialty Store
Dry cleaners (Clothes / Bedding / Draperies / Hangers)	Sporting Event / Practice
Furniture Store	Telephone Office
Garden Shop / Nursery	Theater (Movie or Live performance)
Government Offices	Thrift Store (Drop off donations)
Grocery Store (Grocery List/ Coupons / Money or check / Cooler)	Utility Department
Hardware Store	Veterinarian / Pet Groomer / Pet Store
Insurance Office	Video Store (Tapes / DVD / ID card)
Jewelers	
Landlord / Mortgage Company	**Take Keys:** House, Auto, Mail box, Office
Laundry (Dirty clothes, etc. / Detergent / Fabric Softener / Money / Hangers / Plastic bags / Laundry Basket)	**Take**: Wallet / Purse / Credit or Debit card / Checkbook / Cell phone / Briefcase / Eye glasses / Tissues / Medications / Return merchandise with receipt

WHAT TO TAKE TO WORK

Going to Work for the day:	Keep at work for every day:
Food and drink	Mug or glass
Water bottle	Hand lotion
Clothes for workout	Lip balm
Change of shoes	Medications (if securely locked)
Layered clothing (who knows what the thermostat will be)	Fan or small heater
Keys for desk, office, etc.	Pictures of family, friends, pets
Money for vending machines and meals	Emergency telephone numbers
Laptop computer	Feminine hygiene items
Books and anything you took home that you'll need	Back rest
Planning book or electronic planner	Foot rest
	Facial tissue
	Extra personal items

WHAT TO TAKE ON A PICNIC

Important Items:	Food Preparation and Service:
Blanket	Food and drink (include some water)
Bug repellent	Plastic ware or flatware
Cell telephone	Paper goods: Plates / Cups / Napkins / Towels / Bowls
Extra clothing (layer for all weather types)	Salt and Pepper
Game equipment	Condiments (Mustard, Ketchup, Salsa)
Hat	Chairs and Table
Music--CDs	Firewood and starter
Poncho/ rain coat	Stove / Fuel / Matches
Shade--umbrellas or tarp with rope	Pots and pans
Stroller for baby or children	Pot holders
Sunglasses	Utensils for cooking
Sunscreen	Trash bags
	Cooler and ice

WHAT TO TAKE ON A SHORT HIKE

Important Items:	Sunscreen
Backpack or waterproof bag	Walking cane or stick
Bug repellent	My favorite--a personal water mister
Camera and film	
Cell telephone or GPS locater	
Extra clothing (layer for all weather types)	
Hat	
Knife (Swiss Army or Leather man style)	
Music--CDs	Food Preparation and Service:
Poncho/ rain coat	Food and drink (include lots of water)
Shoes with support or sturdy boots / Socks	Matches
Sunglasses	Trash bags

Safety—

- Check weather reports and flood warnings.
- Stay on established trails.
- Stay away from edges of cliffs with loose rocks or gravel.
- Rest if you become disoriented and drink more water.
- Be aware of children at all times--they get lost in a hurry with tragic results.
- Secure your car keys in a pocket or zippered backpack where they won't drop out someplace along the trail.

WHAT TO TAKE TO AN OUTDOOR CONCERT

Important Items:	Plan for all kinds of weather:
Tickets	Layered clothing
Identification	Rain coat or poncho
Extra car key	Umbrella
Blanket (to sit on or to keep warm)	Gloves and hat
Money for souvenirs and food (Put in a secure place)	Fleece or sweater or coat
Sunglasses	Comfortable walking shoes
Sunscreen	
Food or drink (if allowed)	
Friends	
Binoculars	

TRAVEL AND VACATION

Travel is an adventure. Those vagabonds who look upon it as anything else will be stymied on each trip as reservations are misplaced, cars break down, luggage is lost, or money is stolen. You may find yourself without the key to your locked luggage or the key to the trailer. And the simple things--a forgotten pair of shoes; an unexpected cold--put the damper on many a vacation.

Planning vacations is my downfall. My clothes are always thrown in the luggage the night before I leave on vacation since packing is one task I detest, and I procrastinate. The Packing List is the single most important planning tool I use to make it through a trip. For you travelers who are not sure that vacations or business travels are an adventure, this list will assist you to make it through the days away from home base.

The movie, _The Out of Towner's_ illustrates the fantasy versus reality excursion as the very organized male character deals with the circumstances that overtake him when he steps onto the travel circuit. He encounters airplane delays, crowded trains, reservations let go when he doesn't show up on time, muggers, and other normal travel adventures.

Another realistic travel movie is _Vacation_ with Chevy Chase driving across country with his less than adoring family. His wife begs him to fly to California (obviously she never saw _The Out of Towner's_) but he insists on seeing America through the windshield of his new, truckster wagon. These movies were hits because the audience can empathize with the characters' dilemma. The simple point gleaned from these movies is we all start with high hopes for each vacation. Then circumstances choose another path and we follow along.

The Packing List does take care of one part of your voyage. At least you explore with your vital necessities in hand. Use a new copy of the Packing List each time you arrange a trip. Finally, even if you throw your clothes in the luggage at the last minute, plan the trip before you head to the car or the airport.

Take the list along with you in a purse or briefcase or carry-on luggage. When you arrive at your destination and need to unpack, you will know by glancing at the list where you threw your toothbrush. Make notes in the spaces if you have clothing that requires dry cleaning, a shirt that lost a button when you packed, or a suit that needs lint brushed off before wearing. Sometimes you don't have time to take care of all those details before you jump in a car for a trip. If your suitcases are lost, this list will give you an inventory of the items in the lost suitcase.

In addition there are 5 others Lists to help you pre-plan travel

1. The Things To Do before you leave home so the house is left in good order
2. Travel Tips, ideas from seasoned travelers who know how to avoid some travel problems
3. Instructions for the House Sitter to be left with the person taking care of your home
4. Instructions for the Child Care provider who is staying with your children
5. Baby's Packing List since traveling with an infant requires much pre-planning

Bon Voyage!

Travel Section Includes These Lists:

PACKING LIST

THINGS TO DO BEFORE A SHORT TRIP

THINGS TO DO BEFORE A LONG TRIP

TRAVEL TIPS

INSTRUCTIONS FOR THE HOUSE SITTER

INSTRUCTIONS FOR CHILD CARE

BABY'S PACKING LIST

CAMPING EQUIPMENT LIST

PACKING LIST

Take this list with you on your trip. Make a copy for insurance purposes. Cross off anything you don't need.

Luggage and Backpacks and Boxes	JEWELRY	PERSONAL CARE ITEMS	DON'T FORGET---
PLAN YOUR CLOTHES	Earrings	Contact lenses / Solution / Case	Books / Magazines
Belt / Suspenders	Necklaces	Cream, face / body	Calculator
Coat / Jacket	Rings	Deodorant	Camera / Video camera
Pants / Slacks / Shorts	Watch / Bracelet	Feminine hygiene/Tampons	Camera batteries
Shirts / Blouses	Cuff links / Studs	First aid kit-bandages,	Camera film / video tapes
Skirts / Dresses		Glasses / Sunglasses / Case	Camera lenses / tripod
Sports coat / Blazer	**IMPORTANT PAPERS**	Hair brush / Comb	Cell phone / GPS
Suit--coordinate with shirts	Address book	Hair curlers / curling iron	Clock / travel alarm
Tie / Scarf	Checks	Hair dryer	Computer / Printer
	Credit cards / Debit card	Hair spray / Gel / Mousse	Copy of important papers
ALSO YOU NEED---	Driver's license	Makeup (Face/ Cheek / Eye / Nails)	Dirty clothes bags
Hat / Visor/ Gloves	Itinerary / Reservations	Mirror	Ear plugs / Eye shade
Nightclothes / Pajamas	Maps / Road atlas / Guide book	Razor / Shaving Cream	Games / Cards
Robe	Money--include foreign exchange	Scissors /Tweezers/Nail clippers	Gifts
Scarf	Passport / Visa	Shampoo / Conditioner	Iron, travel / Steamer
Shoes--coordinate colors	Planning calendar / Organizer	Soap / Soap dish	Keys (Car, House, Luggage)
Slippers	Stationery / Pen / Stamps	Sunscreen / Lip balm	Laundry soap / clothesline
Swimsuit / Towel	Telephone card / Dialer	Tissue / Wet wipes/Cotton swabs/cotton balls	Luggage tags
	Tickets	Toothbrush /Toothpaste / Mouthwash / Floss	Radio / CD player / Headphones CDs or Cassette tapes
	Travel Journal / Pen	**Medications**	Sewing kit--shoelaces / safety pins
Underwear	Traveler's checks	*Eye drops*	Umbrella / Rain gear
Briefs / Boxers / Panties	Extras:	*Indigestion reliever*	Wallet / Handbag
Bras / Sports bra / Camisole		*Motion sickness reliever*	
Slips--Full or half		*Nose / Throat / Cough medicine*	
Socks / Pantyhose		*Pain reliever*	
		Prescription medications	
		Vitamins	

THINGS TO DO BEFORE A SHORT TRIP---	THINGS TO DO BEFORE A LONGER TRIP--
• Arrange for pet care. Leave enough food and supplies for all animals.	• Complete the entire list for the short trip.
• Have newspapers and milk picked up and put inside.	• Unplug major appliances.
• Have mail picked up and stored.	• Arrange for lawn care or snow removal--depending on the season.
• Arrange to have plants watered--inside and outside. Include outside grass.	• Pay bills in advance.
• Turn down furnace or air conditioner a few degrees. Turn off space heaters.	• Have money exchanged into foreign currency for any countries where you will travel. Buy traveler's checks.
• Lock all windows and doors in house, garage, sheds.	• Buy a neck pouch or money belt for your cash and valuables.
• Leave itinerary and telephone numbers where you may be reached. Also leave a list of other emergency telephone numbers with a friend.	• Arrange for mail to be forwarded or e-mails to be sent to your travel computer.
• Leave a key or garage remote control with a trusted neighbor or friend.	• Arrange for travel / automobile / health insurance.
• Put a lamp on a timer to turn on at dusk and off hours later.	• Apply for passport and visas. Take along a copy of your birth certificate.
• Make sure faucets (or water), ovens and stoves are turned off.	• Have a medical and dental exam before leaving. Complete vaccinations.
• Forward telephone calls to your travel cell telephone.	• Refill every prescription medication you will need.
• Wash and dry smelly laundry.	• Have extra eyeglasses or contact lenses prepared.
• Take along a credit card, a debit card, and/or cash.	• Check current health problems in areas of the world where you will travel.
• For automobile trips, fill up with gasoline. Top off fluids. Check tire pressure.	• Make reservations for travel, hotels and special events.
• For air/ train/ bus travel--take along your tickets and a picture ID.	
• Throw out perishables.	
• Empty trash receptacles.	

TRAVEL TIPS

1. Plan the contents of your suitcases before you leave. Take only one or two extra pair of shoes--they are heavy. Take fewer clothes--more money.

2. Choose one major color for all your clothes--avoid white since it can stain easily. Coordinate all clothes with this color. Neutrals are great for travel. Do not take along clothes that require too much fabric care.

3. Keep one suitcase or bag with you while on the move. Include the following items in that bag-- Prescription medications; Eyeglasses or contact lenses; Documentation and valuable papers (keep a photocopy in another safe place); Valuables--it's best to leave these at home; Cell phone; Computer; Change of underwear and clothes if there is room; Camera; Anything you can't live without.

4. Do not overfill your shampoo and other liquid bottles. They will expand and contract and leak.

5. In some countries you will need a piece of paper from your physician stating that you require all those medications.

6. Here are some extra items (some strange) that are good to take with you:

- flashlight; night light
- mini-fan
- baby wipes; toilet paper; facial tissue
- clothes pins; safety pins
- instant packages of food
- duct tape
- plastic baggies
- space blanket; inflatable pillow
- hand sanitizer
- electric or telephone converters
- portable door lock
- sink stopper (good for contact lens wearers)
- batteries for all devices you packed

7. Prevent wrinkles by separating clothes with tissue paper or dry cleaner bags.

8. Check the weather forecast for your destination and plan clothes accordingly.

INSTRUCTIONS FOR THE HOUSE SITTER

EMERGENCY CONTACTS: (Name, Address and Telephone Number)	**ITINERARY:** (List city for each day and contact in each city)
My Cell Phone Number:	Departure Date
My Pager Number:	Return Date
My e-mail address:	Sunday
Neighbor	Monday
Relative	Tuesday
Pastor or clergy	Wednesday
Doctor	Thursday
Veterinarian	Friday
Other	Saturday
SPECIAL INSTRUCTIONS: (Cross out ones that don't apply)	Sunday
Water the plants on these days	Monday
Water the grass on these days	Tuesday
Pick up the mail on these days	Wednesday
Bring in newspapers	Thursday
Feed and water dogs (name)	Friday
Feed and water cats (name)	Saturday
Feed and water fish, gerbils, etc.	
Clean house on these days	Home Address:
	Home Telephone #:

Use when you travel and leave someone in charge of your house.

INSTRUCTIONS FOR CHILD CARE

NAMES AND AGES OF CHILDREN:	NAME, ADDRESS AND TELEPHONE NUMBER OF SCHOOLS:
ACTIVITY SCHEDULE FOR CHILDREN:	HOME ACTIVITY SCHEDULE :
	Wake Up Time
	Dinnertime
	Nap Time
	Bed Time
	Television allowed these hours
	Computer games allowed these hours
	NAMES OF APPROVED FRIENDS:
CARPOOL NUMBERS FOR CHILDREN:	
	SPECIAL INSTRUCTIONS:

Use when you travel and leave children at home.

BABY'S PACKING LIST

Name of Child_____

Plan Baby's Food	Needed Per Day	Multiply (x) by days on trip	Equals (=) number needed
Formula (Scoops per day)			# of cans
Juice			# of cans
Bottled water			# of bottles
Can / Jars of baby food			# of jars
Plan Baby's Clothes	**Needed Per Day**	**Multiply (x) by days on trip**	**Equals (=) number needed**
Shirts or tops			
Pants			
Rompers / Creepers / Diaper sets			
Sleepers / Gowns			
Socks / Tights			
Sweaters / Coats			
Dresses / Skirts			
Underwear			
Diapers			
Undershirts / Onesies			
Underpants			

(The total number assumes you will not be able to wash clothes on the trip. Adjust the numbers if you have access to a washer / dryer.)

You will also need:	Personal care items
Backpack or sling	Diaper rash ointment
Blankets	First aid kit-bandages
Bottles / Nipples / Liners / Brush	Hair brush / Comb
Burp pads	Powder / Lotion
Car seat / Carrier	Scissors / Tweezers / Nail clippers
Changing pad	Shampoo
Diaper Bag	Soap / Soap dish
Dirty clothes bags	Sunscreen / Lip balm

You will also need:	Personal care items	
Laundry soap / clothesline	Tissue / Wet wipes / Cotton swabs / Cotton balls	
Pacifier	Toothbrush / Toothpaste	
Plastic bags	Extras	
Sunglasses	**Medications**	
Stroller		
Tickets & Identification (Passport or Birth Certificate)	*Eye drops*	
Toys	*Nose / Throat / Cough medicine*	
More clothes	*Pain reliever*	
Hat / Headbands / Barrettes	*Prescription medications*	
Shoes / Booties	*Vitamins*	
Swimsuit / Towel	Extras	

It takes planning to take a baby or small child on a trip. Use this list with your customized additions.

CAMPING

The light from the setting sun throws mountain peak shadows onto the uneven trails of the isolated campground. Here and there shimmering lights from the now lit fires herald the consummation of another imperturbable day in the Rockies. The darkness settles and heads nod in preparation for restful sleep in the chilled air.

The campers ready themselves and take one last trip through the darkness to use the facilities--but wait. For one camper the niggling feeling becomes reality as he remembers his flashlight is in the garage at home and it is too dark to make it down the trail without some light. Too bad he did not use his Camping List.

Campers forget things all the time. Wanderers have always enjoyed the freedom to rush off to the mountains or beach without preliminary planning. The lack of a match or flashlight in the middle of nowhere may bring frustration, but creativity is part of the camper's creed.

One time a creative camper without a flashlight used his auto's cigarette lighter to ignite a rolled newspaper so he could jog to the outhouse. His solution for getting back to the campsite is speculation. And there are the machine-wise explorers who drive to the rest room and leave on the car lights to guide them down the path. However, a flashlight would be easier.

The Camping Equipment List is to help you remember all the tiny parts around your house that need to go with you on a campout. In addition to supplies, do not forget the clothing and food required for your days away from civilization. The List is a checklist to be marked off as each item is packed. It is also a planning list to be used to gather the tent and sleeping bags together and to make sure you own a propane stove before you set off unprepared.

Most of you using the list will be seasoned campers who know what you need to take along. But many of us forget something because we are in a hurry to get out of town before the Friday night traffic hits the two-lane, winding roads.

CAMPING EQUIPMENT LIST

Camping List--Pack items in car or Pack in trailer or Pack in backpack			
EQUIPMENT		**FOOD PREPARATION**	**EXTRAS**
Air mattress / repair kit / pump	Rope	Aluminum foil / food wrap	Books / Magazines
Ax / hatchet	Sharpening stone	Bowls	Campground directory
Backpack / Knapsack	Shovel / Trowel	Can opener / bottle opener	Cards / games / puzzles
Bag, duffle	Sleeping bag / Blanket / Liner	Coffee pot	Cell phone / GPS
Bags, plastic with ties	Soap / Toiletries--See Travel List	Cooking utensils (fork, knife, spoon)	Guide books
Batteries	Table, folding	Cooking pot / pan	Inflatable pool / Toys
Beach chair / umbrella	Tape, duct or nylon	Cooler / Ice	Licenses / Permits
Binoculars	Tarp / Plastic sheets	Dish soap / detergent / cleanser	Maps / Atlas
Broom	Tent / Poles / Stakes / Rope	Dish towels	Music / CD, cassette player
Bungee cord fasteners	Toilet, portable	Dish pan / basin / drainer	Paper / Pen
Camera / Film	Toilet paper / Seat covers	Flatware (forks, knives, spoon)	Radio / Walkie-talkie
Camp cot	Towels / Wash cloths	Food--use Menu Planner and Grocery	Sports equipment
Candles	Walking pole	Frying pan / Skillet / Griddle	Watch / Clock
Canteen	Water carrier / Water bottle	Fuel / Funnel	Umbrella
Chair	Water purifier / Purification kit / Filter	Glasses / Cups	**CLOTHING**
Charcoal	Whistle	Marshmallow stick / Skewer	Belts / Suspenders
Clothes pins	**FIRST AID KIT**	Matches / Butane lighter	Coat / Jacket / Parka
Compass	Adhesive tape	Measuring spoons / Cups	Dirty clothes bag
Facial tissue / Wet wipes	Aloe Vera gel / Antibiotic cream	Mess kit	Fleece / Shell
Firewood / Fire starters	Antacid	Napkins	Gloves / Mittens
First aid kit	Bandages / Gauze	Paper towels	Hat / Headbands
Fishing /Hunting equipment	Contacts / Solution / Case	Plates	Jeans / Pants / Shorts
Flashlights / Head lamps / Bulbs	Insect repellent	Pot holders	Raingear / Poncho
Foam / Thermal pad	Lip balm	Recipes / Book	Shirts
Fuel / Funnel	Medicines--Eye / Nose / Throat	Reflector oven	Shoes / Boots
Gasoline / kerosene	Pain reliever	Spatula / Pancake turner	Socks
Heater	Prescription medicines	Sponge / scouring pads	Sunglasses / Eyeglasses
Lantern / Mantles	Safety pins	Stove / Grill	Sweaters / Sweatshirts
Matches / Butane lighter	Scissors / Tweezers	Thermal jug / Containers	Swim wear / Sandals
Pillow	Sunscreen	Tongs	Toiletries--See Packing List
Pliers	Wipes / Cleansing pads	Trash bags	Underwear / Long Johns
Pocket knife with added tools			
			Plus your customized items

Entertaining Section Includes These Lists:

PLANNING A PARTY

PARTY BUDGET PLANNER

PLANNING A WEDDING

WEDDING BUDGET PLANNER

PLANNING FOR HOUSE GUESTS

ENTERTAINING

This list is to help you plan anything from a backyard picnic to a Fiftieth Anniversary Party. For a picnic, you would eliminate many of the items listed below. Just cross them off and ignore them. The pre-planning part of the list is standard for almost all events. Also, feel free to change the Dates at the top of the list. Change them to match your time schedule. Have a happy and successful party. At the bottom of the page is a Budget Planner for your convenience.

PLANNING A PARTY						
Setup binder for planning purposes						
☀ PRE-PLANNING: Choose party date and time and length Determine your budget Approximate number of guests to be invited Determine style and theme of party Determine color scheme of party Determine location of party Determine if you will hire party coordinator						
COUNTDOWN ☀	2 Months	1 Month	2 Weeks	1 Week	Days Before	Party Day
☀ Choose final date and time						
☀ Finalize guest list						
☀ Book place for party-- pay fees						
☀ Buy or make invitations						

Send out invitations (or make telephone calls)					
Select and book caterer or prepare menu lists and find kitchen and serving help					
Prepare written outline for party day					
Make food and drink assignments for the party					
Order food and drink					
Pick up food and drink					
Prepare food and drink					
Order or buy plates, flatware, napkins, tablecloths and serving dishes					
Buy or make decorations for tables and serving tables					
Arrange for photographer or prepare cameras with film, batteries and tripods					
Select music					
Order rental equipment (tables, chairs, tents, fountains, gazebos)					
Arrange lodging and transportation for out-of-towners					
Arrange for helpers to clean up					
Give a schedule of the events to all the helpers involved					
Plan games and buy prizes					
Plan extra activities					
Check RSVPs for final guest tally					

PARTY BUDGET PLANNER

Money Needed For This	Estimated Cost of Item	Actual Cost of Item	Running Total of All Items
Invitations			
Postage			
Decorations			
Flowers			
Musicians and entertainment			
Food and Drink			
Cake			
Caterer or Event coordinator			
Rental for event site			
Equipment rental			
Serving staff			
Photographer			
Gifts or prizes for guests			

Your wedding day is one of the most important days of your life. Many friends and family will be involved. Pictures will be taken from all angles by amateur and professional photographers. You will spend more money on this celebration day than any day of your life. You want to plan it so everything will be perfect.

There are hundreds of sources for helping you plan a wedding. This List is a very simplified planning tool so you will know where to begin. Then research in detail each aspect of your plan. Start with a three ring binder or a folder to keep track of all the details that will be involved and you are going to have many business cards and invoices and quotes that you need to store someplace. Put all those pieces of paper in the binder.

PLANNING A WEDDING						
	6-12 Months	4-6 Months	2 Months	2-4 Weeks	1 Week	Wedding Day
Choose Engagement Ring Ask the "Will you marry me?" question in a romantic style						
Pre-Planning Choose wedding date (approximately) Determine your budget Approximate number of guests to be invited Determine style of wedding Determine color scheme of wedding Determine number of attendants Determine location of wedding and reception Determine if you will hire wedding coordinator Plan honeymoon						

☛ Choose final date and time						
☛ Place engagement notice in local newspaper						
☛ Select and book place for wedding ceremony-- arrange for officiator to perform wedding						
☛ Book place for wedding rehearsal						
☛ Select and book place for reception--pay deposit						
☛ Select and book place for rehearsal dinner or bridal showers--pay fees						
☛ Book honeymoon travel, hotels, and special event tickets--pay fees						
☛ Get passports and visas for honeymoon						
☛ Choose and order wedding dress, veil, shoes, lingerie and accessories						
☛ Final fittings for clothing						
☛ Pick up bride's dress and accessories--final payment						
☛ Select attendants						
☛ Select bridesmaids' dresses--get swatch to match ribbon, shoes, etc						
☛ Order bridesmaids' dresses						
☛ Pick up bridesmaids' dresses						
☛ Order groom's clothing						
☛ Final haircut, etc. for groom						
☛ Order ushers' clothing						
☛ Pick up groom/ushers' clothing						
☛ Help mothers and fathers with wedding clothing selections						
☛ Compile guest list from bride						

✒ Compile guest list from groom						
✒ Select invitations						
✒ Order invitations, name tags, place cards, maps, printed napkins, thank you notes and stationery						
✒ Address and mail invitations						
✒ Select and book caterer--if not using caterer, select menus and find kitchen and serving help and bartender						
✒ Order food and drink						
✒ Gather food and drink						
✒ Prepare seating arrangement						
✒ Prepare food and drink						
✒ Order/buy plates, flatware, napkins, tablecloths and serving dishes						
✒ Choose wedding cake, order						
✒ Pick up wedding cake						
✒ Buy and decorate cake knife						
✒ Select and book florist						
✒ Order flower arrangements, bouquets, boutonnieres						
✒ Pick up floral arrangements						
✒ Select and book photographer and video photographer						
✒ Select and book entertainment, DJ and musicians						
✒ Select music for ceremony and reception						
✒ Order rental equipment (tables, chairs, tents, fountains, gazebos)						

☛Purchase and make decorations for wedding and reception					
☛Select and order wedding rings--insurance on rings					
☛ Purchase marriage license--have blood test (check the requirements for your state)					
☛ Arrange lodging for attendants					
☛Rent limousines					
☛ Arrange transportation for attendants and out-of-towners.					
☛Arrange for valet parking					
☛ Choose hair style and make up style for wedding day. Make appointments for manicure, etc.					
☛Buy bride's trousseau					
☛Buy garter and "throw" bouquet					
☛ Buy & wrap thank you gifts for attendants and favors for guests					
☛Attend marital counseling classes					
☛ Meet with lawyer, doctor, dentist					
☛ Find something old, new, borrowed and blue for tradition					
☛ Purchase guest book and pen					
☛ Write vows					
☛ Give participants in wedding and reception a written schedule of the day's events					
☛ Rent or borrow truck to get all items to wedding and reception					

☛ Pay fee to marriage officiator						
☛Pick up tickets for honeymoon						
☛ Pack for honeymoon						
☛Arrange new home for newlyweds						
☛Arrange transportation for newlyweds to new home						
☛ Put wedding announcement in newspaper (may need photo)						
☛Preserve flowers						
☛Review and order photographs						
☛Have wedding gown and veil cleaned and preserved						
☛Record gifts as they are opened						
☛ Write thank you notes for gifts and kindness gifts						

If you want my opinion, the expense of a wedding should be divided equally between the bride's side and the groom's side. No longer is the bride a commodity to be sold and her family shouldn't have to shoulder the majority of the expense. With that said, a lot of people do not agree with me and they want to know the traditional expense breakdown. This list tells you traditionally who should pay for what.

The Bride pays for this	The Groom pays for this
Invitations, postage, stationery, thank you notes, etc.	Engagement and wedding rings for bride
Bride's dress, veil, lingerie, shoes and accessories and her trousseau	Rehearsal dinner or luncheon before the ceremony
Clothing for bride's family	Groom's suit or tuxedo, shoes and accessories
Fees for rental of church or site of ceremony	Clothing for groom's family
Fees for musicians at ceremony	Marriage license
Decorations and rentals at ceremony site	Fee to officiator of ceremony
Fees for rental of reception site	Bride's bouquet
Food, drink, and decorations for reception	Corsages for mothers and boutonnieres for ushers
Wedding cake	Honeymoon
Fees for musicians and entertainment at reception	Wedding gifts for attendants, bride
Floral bouquets for bridesmaids, flower girls	Photograph prints chosen by groom's family
Floral arrangements for ceremony and reception	
Photographer including engagement, wedding and video	
Wedding ring for groom	
Transportation to ceremony and reception (limousines)	
Wedding gifts for attendants, groom	
Preservation of wedding dress and flowers	
Photograph prints chosen by bride's family	
Wedding consultant	
Caterer	

Attendants pay for this

Bridesmaids for their dresses, shoes and accessories	Ushers for their formalwear rental, shoes and accessories
Bridesmaids host a bridal shower	Ushers host a bachelor party
Wedding gift for bride and groom	

WEDDING BUDGET PLANNER

How Much Wedding Can You Afford	Dollar amount of contribution	Date you will have the money
Bride will contribute this amount	$	
Groom will contribute this amount	$	
Bride's parents will contribute this amt	$	
Groom's parents will contribute this amt	$	
Family or friends have pledged this amt	$	
Total Amount Available	$	

Money Needed For This	Estimated Cost of Item	Actual Cost of Item	Running Total of All Items
Invitations			
Postage			
Decorations			
Flowers, corsages, etc.			
Musicians and entertainment			
Food			
Drink			
Wedding cake			
Caterer			
Serving staff			
Rental for wedding site			
Rental for reception site			
Equipment rental			
Wedding dress			

Money Needed For This	Estimated Cost of Item	Actual Cost of Item	Running Total of All Items
Clothing accessories (bride)			
Clothing, groom			
Photographer			
Wedding rings			
Transportation			
Wedding consultant			
Thank you gifts			
Fees to clergy or judge			
Honeymoon--travel, lodging, etc.			
Parties, luncheons, dinners			
License and fees			

PLANNING FOR HOUSE GUESTS

When visitors are coming to stay at your house, your routine is changed and your workload increases. Prepare before they come with this list. The list is set up so you can plan one week ahead and mark which day you can complete each item. If you have more time than one week to prepare, change the headings to fit your schedule.

PLANNING FOR HOUSE GUESTS	Mon	Tues	Wed	Thurs	Fri	Sat	Sun	Later
Let guests know dates house is available								
Arrange days off from work								
Ask guests about food allergies								
Plan your meals using the Menu Planners Easy breakfast foods, sandwiches for lunch								
Buy extra food staples, paper goods, toilet paper, snacks, punch, soda, juices								
Use paper plates, cups, napkins if possible								
Buy groceries using the Grocery List								
Prepare meals ahead, freeze								
Ask guests about other allergies (pets, etc.)								
Make arrangements for their pets								
Arrange transportation (taxi, rental, etc.)								
Reserve tickets for local attractions								
Basic house clean:								
Vacuum floors, furniture								
Dust, Straighten								
Wash towels, sheets, blankets								
Clean toilets, shower/tub, surfaces								
Straighten kitchen								
Mop floors								
Arrange extra items for guest:								
Toothbrush and paste								
Razors								

PLANNING FOR HOUSE GUESTS	Mon	Tues	Wed	Thurs	Fri	Sat	Sun	Later
Toiletries (Shampoo, soap, etc.)								
Blankets and pillows								
Towels, washcloths								
Alarm clock								
Plan sleeping arrangements--check with family								
Check inflatable mattress for leaks								
Plan dining arrangements--more chairs at table								
Have spare key made								
Make list of important telephone numbers								
Give them copy of your schedule:								
Meal times, Work times, Church, Sports events								
Plan for laundry, extra quarters for Laundromat								
Stay calm in the midst of chaos								
Have extra cash on hand								

CHRISTMAS AND HOLIDAYS

Happy Holidays! The music and the joyful spirit are in the air and millions of people are preparing for the big celebration. The oven stands ready for your pound cake and brownies, only don't forget that your best friend told you that she is lactose intolerant and your milk-laden cookies made her sick last year. So you will need to find a new recipe. And your aunt told you not to send her peanut brittle again because it pulled on her dentures.

The gifts need to be purchased, and your father's new wife told you, "We will be doing the tree in purple colors this year, so only give us coordinating colored decorations." At work you were caught short on presents last year, so you need to buy extra tins of nuts just in case someone in the mail room gives you jelly beans again. The children need 52 cupcakes each, plus their special teacher gifts for their primary teacher, their physical education teacher, their music teacher and the principal. The kids told you, "We want presents for Fido, Kitty, and Goldy," their pets. In addition they have a gift exchange for secret pals and they need a small, wrapped present for each of the five days before vacation.

The Holiday cards need to be mailed out early and last year you were smart enough to buy them on the half-price sale after Christmas and you packed them in a box where you can find the greeting cards. Only your last year's cards have silver-trim that is out of style since the current cards are all gold-trimmed.

And you need to remember to get to the post office for the Christmas stamps since you waited until December last year and the stamps were sold out. Plus you have to get to the printers to order your snowflake Holiday address labels for the envelopes.

Welcome to a contemporary Holiday season! Your mother never could have anticipated this version of the Holidays. Christmas is big business--big family and friends' business, big childhood expense business and big stress and disappointment business. Christmas is listed as one of the top 100 stress producing incidents of life. Most people's advice for getting through Christmas is consistent--simplify, cut back, do not overdo. Good luck. The demands are still evident and the pressure is on you to succeed, to make everyone happy, except maybe yourself.

Men reading this page may not understand my interpretation of Christmas bliss because it has been American tradition for the women and mothers to take over Christmas. As traditions change and males are without a woman in their lives, they too are becoming Christmas tragedies, trying to accomplish too much in too little time.

Remember how disgusted people used to be when the Christmas decorations came out before Thanksgiving. Any summertime shopper at the mall knows that Christmas ornaments are displayed in July and you need to purchase your yearly, dated ornament early before other collectors snatch them up.

The Holiday lists are to help traditional moms or untraditional men and women get a grip on the unbelievable requirements of the holiday season. First, the lists help you put a perspective on the holidays and let you embrace what is most important to your celebration. Second, the lists help you in holiday planning so the work is dispersed throughout the year.

The Holiday Lists become a great friend to you in accomplishing a multitude of tasks early enough so December does not become a winter flurry of days lost in shopping, mailing, partying and wrapping.

When you have extra storage space, it's okay to buy presents early and to have them wrapped and hidden. Shopping for presents is one of the easiest things to do before December since the stores are full of wonderful merchandise no matter what season of the year it is. However, if you enjoy the rush of Christmas shopping, plan your gift shopping trips in December. As always, the Lists let you customize your own plan.

As you buy presents, fill in your **Gift Lists** located in the next section of the book describing what has been purchased and you will never forget that you bought Aunt Mary a piece of jewelry at an estate sale in May and wanted to give it to her in December. There are two styles of Holiday Gift Lists--one for close friends and family and one for acquaintances who receive one or two gifts from you or your family.

The **Holiday Planning Budget** enables you to keep a running list of every item you purchase for this season. You may want to include only the large items or you may want to include each small purchase.

There is a **Holiday Card List.** And, of course, there are the Holiday To-Do Lists--Pre-holiday; Holiday To-Do; After the Holiday--that will help you schedule your calendar. **It's a Feast!** in the food section helps you plan those large Thanksgiving or Holiday dinners and never again forget the whipped cream. **Holiday Party Planner**, used in conjunction with the **Party Planning List** makes party time easier.

The **Homemade Baking/ Candy List** allows you to plan your baking needs for the year and arrange the ingredients for easy cookie exchanges or neighborhood homemade candy gifts.

Decide which of these charts and lists fit your requirements. Ignore those that don't help you. Fill in those that make life easier. Design your own plan to make this year a planned, organized year.

Christmas and Holidays Includes These Lists:

PRE-HOLIDAY PLANNER

HOLIDAY TO-DO LIST

HOLIDAY BUDGET

HOMEMADE BAKING / CANDY LIST

HOLIDAY CARD LIST

HOLIDAY PARTY PLANNER

AFTER THE HOLIDAY TO-DO LIST

PRE-HOLIDAY PLANNER

Getting the Kitchen Ready:	Getting the Dining Room Ready:
Polish appliances including refrigerator, dishwasher, stove and hood, microwave, and small, countertop appliances	Take out holiday tablecloths, place mats, etc. for October and November holidays.
Clean the oven	Locate china and crystal for holidays--Wash
Polish cabinet doors and handles	Locate silverware or special flatware--Wash
Straighten interior of cabinets and drawers.	Polish silver--flatware and serving pieces
Sharpen knives	Wash tablecloths, place mats, pot holders, etc.
Deep clean kitchen floor	Dust or clean chandeliers
Locate special serving pieces--Wash	Polish table, hutch, buffet, etc.
	Make place cards for tables
Getting the House Ready:	Plan candles and floral arrangements
Vacuum or dust near the moldings on floors	Plan extra chairs for guests
Put away the junk from summertime	Deep clean dining room carpet or floor
Deep clean the guest bathroom	Throw out broken, chipped dishes & glasses
Clean fireplace and chimney. Buy wood and starter fuel.	Buy new dishes, glasses, flatware, candles, etc.
Dust figurines / ceramics / decorations	**The Food**
Discard magazines and papers	Plan big menus using It's A Feast menu planner
For deep cleaning use Home Maintenance List	Purchase non-perishable food items on sale
Plan parties using the Entertain/Party List	Delegate food and dish assignments to family and friends
	Plan serving dishes and serving pieces

HOLIDAY TO-DO LIST

What Needs To Be Done--Plan Your Work (Cross out tasks that you will not be doing this year)	Target Date to be completed--Schedule Work	Who will be completing this task?	Check When Finished
Address holiday cards / stamps / return address labels / photo			
and Mail holiday cards			
Clean the house--use the House Maintenance Lists			
Cut Christmas tree			
Decorate Christmas tree			
Decorate inside the house			
Decorate outside the house / yard			
Deliver gifts			
Exchange names for group giving			
Make baked goods			
Make decorations / ornaments			
Make holiday cards			
Make gifts / gift wrap / crafts			
Make holiday recipe binder			
Make memory scrap book			
Organize gift wrap box			
Plan budget for this year			
Plan entertaining / schedule dates--use Party Planner			
Plan food and menu lists			
Plan travel			
Print holiday address labels			
Print holiday pre-printed cards			
Print holiday letter--plan and write letter			
Print photo greeting cards			
Purchase beverages			
Purchase candles			
Purchase decorations / ornaments			
Purchase holiday cards			
Purchase food			
Purchase film, camera, batteries			
Purchase flowers, evergreen boughs, mistletoe			

What Needs To Be Done--Plan Your Work (Cross out tasks that you will not be doing this year)	Target Date to be completed--Schedule Work	Who will be completing this task?	Check When Finished
Purchase gifts--keep track of gifts as they are purchased. Use Gift Lists in book.			
Plan travel days for buying gifts at out-of-town stores			
Purchase gifts from catalogs and from the Internet			
Purchase gift certificates			
Purchase gift wrap, ribbons, tags, etc			
Purchase holiday stamps			
Purchase holiday table linens			
Purchase mailing supplies			
Purchase stocking stuffer gifts			
Purchase tickets to holiday music and drama presentations			
Purchase Christmas tree			
Schedule babysitters			
Schedule Christmas caroling			
Schedule family photo			
Schedule religious activities			
Schedule time for family			
Schedule time for relaxation			
Schedule visit to hospital or nursing home for service			
Schedule volunteer work			
Wrap gifts			
Extras:			
This list is alphabetized and not categorized with first things first. Plan your personalized timetable using the 2nd column. *If you come from a part of the world with different traditions, change the list to fit your individual holiday plans. Happy holidays.*			

HOLIDAY BUDGET

Estimated Holiday Budget $_____

ITEM TO BUY	ESTIMATED COST $	ACTUAL COST $	TOTAL AMOUNT SPENT
Example: Evergreen bough	$10	$8.27	$8.27
Tree lights	$20	$26.00	+ $34.27

Holiday Planning Budget to be used for Total Holiday expenses. List gifts, cards, stamps, baking goods, food, etc. You will have an estimated amount to be spent and an actual amount spent for the year.

HOMEMADE BAKING/CANDY LIST

#____

Name of Item _____	Gift For ⇓	Need by (Date) ⇓	When Delivered ⇓
⇓Ingredients ⇓			

#____

Name of Item _____	Gift For ⇓	Need by (Date) ⇓	When Delivered ⇓
⇓Ingredients ⇓			

Use these lists to keep track of your homemade goodies for the Holidays.
- List the name of the item (Example: Chocolate Fudge).
- List the name of each person who will receive the homemade food item (Column 2). Room for 7 names.
- Indicate the date you need to deliver the item (Column 3); this is helpful since some items need to be prepared the day of delivery and you need baking time scheduled that day.
- Mark Column 4 when you have delivered or mailed the homemade item.
- Column 1 is to list the ingredients needed to make the item. Transfer this list to your grocery store list after you have determined amounts needed to make enough for all your friends on the list.

HOLIDAY CARD LIST

Names on this Page (Circle One) ABC *DEF* GHI *JKL* MNO *PQR* STU *VW* XYZ

Name	Family Members --Names / Year Born
Address	1.
City/State/Zip	2.
Telephone	3.
Years Card Sent:	4.
Years Card Received:	5.

Name	Family Members --Names / Year Born
Address	1.
City/State/Zip	2.
Telephone	3.
Years Card Sent:	4.
Years Card Received:	5.

Name	Family Members --Names / Year Born
Address	1.
City/State/Zip	2.
Telephone	3.
Years Card Sent:	4.
Years Card Received:	5.

Name	Family Members --Names / Year Born
Address	1.
City/State/Zip	2.
Telephone	3.
Years Card Sent:	4.
Years Card Received:	5.

HOLIDAY PARTY PLANNER

Date of Party:_____ Time:_____

Place:_____ Hosted by:_____

GUEST LIST

Name	Address	Telephone	Inv.	Yes/No

Column 1 Name of Guests. Column 2 Address. Column 3 Telephone Number.
Column 4, Mark when invitation is sent.
Column 5 Keep track of Yes/No responses to invitation.
Use **Party Planner List** in the Entertaining Section

AFTER THE HOLIDAY TO-DO LIST

What Needs To Be Done--Plan Your Work (Cross out tasks that you will not be doing this year)	Target Date to be completed-- Schedule Work	Who will be completing this task?	☑ When Finished
Add photos to album or scrap book			
Buy discounted presents for next year's gifts			
Clean the house--use the House Cleaning Lists			
Dispose of used, live tree			
Draw names for family gift exchanges next year			
File new holiday recipes			
Film developed and picked up--enlargements made			
Make gifts / gift wrap / crafts			
Make holiday recipe binder			
Make memory scrap book			
Open bank account for next year's holiday savings plan			
Organize gift wrap box			
Organize Holiday planner for next year--keep track of gifts			
Plan budget for next year			
Plan family get to together during year for holiday photo			
Purchase candles / cards / decorations / ornaments / gift wrap at after Holiday sales			
Put away dishes, linens and tableware			
Record new addresses for friends--from their cards			
Return gifts for exchange or refund			
Store artificial tree			
Un-decorate the Christmas tree			
Un-decorate inside the house			
Un-decorate outside the house / yard			
Write thank you notes--mail			

GIFTS

Several years ago, it was considered proper to choose the wrapping paper and ribbons for a gift as meticulously as the gift that went inside the gift wrap. Today, we buy colored, shiny bags, toss the gift inside, cover it with some sparkly shredded paper and take it along to the party. This change was for the better and a great time saver. Purists still choose to wrap with paper and bows, yet they may now top the package with ribbon roses made in far away factories. Everybody loves to cut corners without looking tasteless.

Another change in gift-giving is the quantity of gifts which are handed out each year. Children attend countless birthday parties; adults hold "Over-the Hill" parties; new house warming presents are required; retirement parties, new baby showers, or wedding receptions require remembrances. Each month is filled with gift-giving opportunities.

The giver of gifts may find these celebrations cropping up constantly while shopping and wrapping each present demands time. Precious time slips away unless you plan ahead for all these occasions. Of course the Internet has made shopping for gifts a little easier.

Buying Gifts Before You Need Them

A personalized gift for each person sounds like a noble idea. Unless you have unlimited time for shopping, forget that idea. Instead find one, similar gift that will be sent for each occasion. Florists and catalogue food distributors increased their business when people caught on to this idea.

Everyone on your gift list gets a box of candy or a cheese tray or a bouquet of flowers, ordered by you at the appropriate time during the year. No fuss, no hassle. All you have to do is write down on your calendar the date the gift needs to arrive and schedule your telephone call to place the order early in that month. Always schedule that telephone call on your planner or To-Do Lists when you look over the month and recognize a gift-giving affair.

Cash is handy for this type of giving and etiquette allows money orders or cash or gift certificates to be sent for the special day. Card stores carry special money sized greeting cards to hold the bills or check. Gift certificates fit inside these envelopes also. Schedule on your planner the date you need to buy the certificate and mail the card.

The second way to buy gifts ahead of time requires a little more planning. Included in this chapter is a Gift List—For Family / Friends to help you planning. The first line names the recipient of the gift(s). The next line is for the date of the birthday, then the date of the anniversary, and you may add other important dates in that person's life. For example, you may send a card each year in remembrance of the loss of a spouse. Mark that date in the same space. The person's clothes sizes may be entered on the next line.

Below that space is a Wish List area. Fill this in during the year when the person tells you about something they would love to receive. Jot down ideas and interests for that person.

The next four lines list your purchases for that person. You may estimate the projected price that you would like to spend and enter it in the column, second from the right. The third column gives you a space to record the actual money spent on the article. The fourth column is for checking off when the present gets purchased and wrapped (and mailed, if necessary).

Continuing down the list, the seventh box says Cake, and would be completed if you need to buy or make a cake for the party. The last line lists the cost of food for the party. The menu would be planned on a Menu List.

This Gift List assists you in planning the gifts for each person's special day or days. Duplicate the list and fill in one before the special day. Keep the lists in a binder so they may be referred to as gifts are purchased. Keep this list hidden unless you want everyone to know what you bought them and how much it cost.

Gifts, Wrapped and Ready

Shopping days are fewer each year since we spend our leisure time in sports, in traveling or relaxing. On those days when you have a chance to make it to the shopping mall or one of your favorite stores, take along your completed Gift List and shop for items on each Wish List. Ideas will pop into your head as you go from store to store and add those ideas to the wish lists.

Purchase items you can afford to buy now, or put them on layaway for later pickup. Mark on your Lists what item you would like to come back to buy. The name of the store where the item may be purchased can be shown on the List.

When your shopping unearths a bargain, purchase it now even if the date for the special occasion remains a few months future in the calendar. Record the gift on your list and you will remember that you have that gift ready.

Sometimes bargains are good for more than one person or you contemplate giving a comparable present to other people on your lists. Buy while the bargain is hot and store the presents until you need an emergency gift. Record on your Extra Gifts I've Purchased what you have packed away for important presents.

The Extra Gift List helps you keep track of miscellaneous gifts you purchase during the year and hope to be able to use later. It is easy to forget what was purchased, so this list keeps track of what was bought, when it was purchased, and where it is stored. Also you may indicate if the gift would be appropriate for an anniversary, a birthday, at Christmas, or a baby gift. The last column is available to mark when the gift is given away and you can tell if you need to replenish your supply of "extra" gifts.

Perhaps you like to buy ahead yet you do not want to bother with a list of prospective gifts. Make sure you keep all the gifts in one box or one area so you can open the box and pluck out something in an emergency. You may want to wrap the presents before storing them so they are ready to be given. Indicate on the package wrapping what is contained inside.

Gifts Section Includes These Lists:

GIFT WRAP

GIFT LIST—FAMILY / CLOSE FRIENDS

GIFT LIST—ONE PRESENT PER RECIPIENT

EXTRA GIFTS I'VE PURCHASED

GIFT GIVING PROJECT LIST

GIFT WRAP

A small gift wrap assortment should be assembled for each household.

GIFT WRAP TO BUY	AMOUNT TO PURCHASE	☑ WHEN PURCHASED
Gift wrap, flat sheet/rolls 　Anniversary 　Baby gift 　Birthday 　Feminine 　Graduation 　Holiday / Seasonal 　Juvenile 　Masculine 　Shower 　Wedding		
Gift sacks		
Bows, pre-made		
Ribbon, spools		
Shredded, colored paper		
Tissue paper		
Gift enclosure cards		
Greeting cards		
Decorative tags		
Bow maker		
Gift boxes		

GIFT LIST—FAMILY / CLOSE FRIENDS

NAME BIRTHDAY ANNIVERSARY CLOTHES SIZE	PROJECTED $ SPENT	ACTUAL $ SPENT	☑
WISH LIST			
PRINCIPAL GIFT			
GIFT			
GIFT			
GIFT			
CAKE			
FOOD			

NAME BIRTHDAY ANNIVERSARY CLOTHES SIZE	PROJECTED $ SPENT	ACTUAL $ SPENT	☑
WISH LIST			
PRINCIPAL GIFT			
GIFT			
GIFT			
GIFT			
CAKE			
FOOD			

HOLIDAY GIFT LIST
(One present per recipient)

NAME OF RECIPIENT	$ AMT	MAIL DATE	GIFT DESCRIPTION	☑

EXTRA GIFTS I'VE PURCHASED

DATE	DESCRIPTION OF GIFT	PLACE STORED	TYPE	☑ GIVEN

GIFT GIVING PROJECT LIST

Description of Project:	$ TO-BE SPENT	ACTUAL $ SPENT	☑
Supplies Needed for Project: _____ _____ _____ _____ _____	_____ _____ _____ _____	_____ _____ _____ _____	
Project Start Date:			
Project Completion Date:			
Finished product to be given to: 1._____ 2._____ 3._____ 4._____ 5._____	**Projected Date**	**Wrapped & Given**	

Description of Project:	$ TO-BE SPENT	ACTUAL $ SPENT	☑
Supplies Needed for Project: _____ _____ _____ _____ _____	_____ _____ _____ _____	_____ _____ _____ _____	
Project Start Date:			
Project Completion Date:			
Finished product to be given to: 1._____ 2._____ 3._____ 4._____ 5._____	**Projected Date**	**Wrapped & Given**	

MOVING

In the Sixties Decade, freedom was the watch cry which meant waking up in the morning, rolling up your sleeping bag, and taking off for new adventure. That generation grew up, had children, became consumers, and accumulated a household of treasures and junk. Now these free spirits faint at the prospect of moving to a new home since responsibility of ownership surrounds them. No more is it possible to take off without planning the move, taking an inventory, and listing financial alternatives. Moving a household is not fun anymore.

Yet America, and much of the world, stays on the move looking for new employment, new adventure, renewal of family relationships, or 100 other incentives for moving. Before you decide to sell all your furniture and belongings at a garage sale, give the rest to charity and go back to basics, realize that you can make a move almost pleasant by coming up with a strategy for your migration. Disasters in moving happen too often because people try to pick up and leave a home with no preparation.

Moving lends itself easily to a pre-planned list. The Moving Chart helps you plan and schedule your move far enough ahead that it doesn't overwhelm you. You choose which chores need to be done for your move. You decide how far ahead those tasks need to be done before your move. You make decisions that stretch the work out over enough days so you do not feel disheartened. Moving is still a big obligation and entails mounds of work, but feeling you have control of the situation may help.

The Moving Organizer is to be used as a planning system and as a check-off when done system. It lists several common tasks most people undertake when moving. The first three pages have a place for marking when that chore will be completed. The pre-arranged choices are 3 months, 1 month, 2 weeks, 1 week, day before, and moving day. You may change this time table to fit your schedule. These times indicate how far before the move you plan to complete the tasks. Select one of the choices for each chore you wish to complete. Since your move is unique, your schedule and choices will be unique.

Moving Section Includes These Lists:

MOVING ORGANIZER

MOVING A PET

FIRST TO BE UNPACKED

NEW HOME TO-DO LIST

CHANGE OF ADDRESS CARDS

VALUABLES MOVING LIST

PACKING SUPPLIES LIST

MOVING ORGANIZER

Everyone needs a 3-ring binder or folder as a holding place to keep track of the many pieces of paper related to a move. Keep these papers together and save yourself hours of frustration when you need to find a form as you are rushed and panicked. The list below includes papers you may want to collect for this binder or folder.

1. Floor plan of new home

2. IRS form for moving expenses #3903, Publication #521

3. Information from employer on move if employer is paying for move.

4. Travel reservations and tickets

5. Emergency addresses and telephone numbers

6. Papers from moving company:

>   Estimate (binding or non-binding)
>   Bill of lading
>   Information from moving van weigh-ins
>   Inventory
>   Liability coverage
>   Name, address, telephone number of new agent
>   Name of van driver, license number of van
>   Number of shipment
>   Route driver will take

7. IRS form #2119, Sale of Home

8. Papers relating to purchase and sale of homes.
   Keep these in a secure place.

>   Sales contract
>   Homeowner's insurance policy
>   Title insurance policy
>   Warranty deed
>   Closing statement
>   Promissory Note
>   Trust Deed

MOVING TASKS--TO BE DONE	3 MONTHS	1 MONTH	2 WEEKS	1 WEEK	FEW DAYS	MOVE DAY
Place an "X" in the box when you will do each of these tasks. This is your moving plan As each task is completed, check it off Mark out those items that do not pertain to your move.						
Set up 3-ring binder for papers						
Plan move with family						
Get estimates from moving companies						
Reserve truck for self-move						
Buy padlock for rental truck						
Sell house / or end rental agreement						
Buy new house or find new apartment						
Collect boxes and packing materials						
Get information on move from employer						
Make home inventory						
Have appraisal on valuables						
Return borrowed items						
Collect items others have borrowed						
Clear out--Have garage sale. Give to charity. Trip to trash dump.						
Goodbye party for friends						
Dispose of flammables						
Drain gas & oil in lawn mower, snow blower						
Sell club memberships						
Use stored foods						
Arrange for house cleaning service						
Have auto serviced--if driving.						
Arrange ride to airport--if flying						
Clean oven and range						
Defrost refrigerator and freezer. Clean						
Brace washer tub						
Unplug televisions and appliances						
Plan food for moving day						
Plan clothes for travel days						
Do pre-move laundry. Dry cleaning						
Give away plants--or prepare for move						
Take breakables out of drawers--pack.						
Remove decorative light switches / electric cover plates / light fixtures						
Arrange for child care						
Arrange for Pets Moving Necessities						
Buy traveler's checks or get cash for move						
Empty safe-deposit box						
Close bank accounts						
Get copy of medical / dental records						
Grandfather clock / pool table / piano crated (plus other hard to ship items)						

MOVING TASKS--TO BE DONE	3 MONTHS	1 MONTH	2 WEEKS	1 WEEK	FEW DAYS	MOVE DAY
Drain and disassemble water beds						
Pack linens from beds--pack separately						
Pack the automobiles						
Put out trash						
Vacuum / clean rooms						
Pack suitcases to take with you						
Cancel service for cable television service						
Cancel gardening service						
Cancel home deliveries (milk, newspaper, etc.)						
Cancel telephone service						
Cancel trash removal						
Disconnect utilities						
Forward mail / Discontinue post office box						
Change magazine subscriptions						
Send Change of Address to friends / relatives						
Final check of every room and closet						
Close and lock windows. Lock house. Turn in keys.						

NECESSITIES FOR MOVING A PET

	Be sure you have these items for your pet
Arrange for kennel or restrain pet during moving day	Bed / Bedding
Arrange for transportation for pet (Buy pet carrier)	Carrying case / Kennel
Drain aquariums. Secure fish safely for move	Dishes
Clean cages of hamsters, gerbils, birds, etc.	Food / Water
Arrange for moving dog houses or aquariums	Health certificates
	Identification tags
	Immunizations up-to-date
	Kitty litter
	Leash
	Pooper scooper
	Sedative
	Travel reservations
	Veterinarian records

You need a special box or two packed with articles that are needed instantly when you arrive at your new home. This list is to help you plan what will go into those boxes. Isolate those boxes so they do not get packed with all your other belongings. Pack them in the car or keep them handy in the moving truck.

FIRST TO BE UNPACKED ITEMS	
Alarm clock	
Bathroom supplies (Shower curtain, Soap, Toilet Paper, Towels)	Pet food (plus food and water dishes)
Bottle opener / Can opener	Radio (battery operated)
Candles / Flashlight	Shelf paper
Cleaning supplies (Bags / Broom / Cleansers / Dustpan / Mop / Paper towels/ Rags / Sponge / Toilet bowl cleaner)	Suitcases with clothes and toiletries (Eyeglasses / Shampoo / Toothbrush / Toothbrush /
Cooking pot / pan	Telephones / Telephone book
Cooking utensils (Knife / Ladle / Pot holders / Spatula / Spoon)	Tools: Hammer / Nails / Picture hooks / Pliers / Scissors / Screwdriver / Screws / Tape / Tape measure / Wrench
Cups / Glasses / Plates / Napkins	
Extension cords	
First aid kit (Bandages / Pain reliever / Prescription meds)	
Flatware (Forks / Knives / Spoons)	
Food (Plus drinks and snacks)	
Games and toys for children	
Keys for new house or apartment	
Light bulbs	
Linens (Towels / Sheets / Pillows / Blankets)	
Map of new city	
Papers--(Check book / Credit cards / Moving documents)	
Payment for movers	

NEW HOME TO-DO LIST	
Check off inventory list--double check it all	Put on decorative light switches / electric cover plates / light fixtures
Pay moving van driver--some will not take a check	Open bank accounts / Safe deposit box
Return rental truck	Unpack--as you find the time
Buy groceries	Assemble shelving
Reconnect appliances	Hang pictures and posters
Connect utilities	Register for schools
Connect telephone service / Internet service	Start trash removal
Connect cable television	Start home deliveries
Contact Motor Vehicle Department (License plates / Drivers license)	Start mail delivery.
Change locks / Garage door remote control codes	

CHANGE OF ADDRESS CARDS

• Accountant	• Magazine subscriptions (Send address label)
• Attorney	• Newspapers
• Banks / Credit Unions / Savings and Loans	• Optometrist
• Cable television company	• Pharmacist
• Church	• Post Office
• Clubs	• Professional organizations
• Credit card accounts	• Relatives
• Creditors	• Telephone companies
• Dairy	• Trash removal service
• Dentist	• Schools
• Diaper service	• Social security
• Doctors--Primary Care and Specialists	• Stockbrokers
• Employer--Personnel office	• Veterinarian
• Friends	• Voter registration
• Gardener	
• Household help	
• Insurance companies	
• Internet provider	
• Motor Vehicle Department (in person)	

Certain valuables need to be hand carried by you or shipped by security methods. The VALUABLES MOVING LIST helps you determine which objects need special care to be moved.

VALUABLES MOVING LIST

SPECIAL CARE VALUABLE	MOVE: YES OR NO	* WHEN PACKED
Appraisals of valuables		
Bank account books		
Cameras		
Coin/ Stamp collections		
Home inventory or video		
Insurance policies		
Jewelry		
Keys--house/ car/ luggage		
Medical/ Dental records		
Personal files: Birth/ Death/ Marriage certificates Military records Passports/ Visas Wills		
Precious metals		
Safe deposit box contents		
School records		

PACKING SUPPLIES

ITEM NEEDED	HOW MANY I NEED	* WHEN PURCHASED
Small boxes (13 X 13 X 16)		
Medium boxes (18 x 18 x 16)		
Large boxes (18 x 18 x 24)		
Wardrobe boxes (21 x 24 x 48)		
Dish Packs (18 x 18 x 30)		
Mirror/Picture Box		
Mattress Carton		
Newspaper/packing paper		
Trash bags/twist ties		
Bubble wrap/ Styrofoam pellets		
Packing tape		
Scissors/Utility Knife		
Felt tip marker		
Rope		
Furniture pads / blankets / or carpet pad		
Plastic shrink wrap or meat wrap to protect furniture, lamps, mirrors, etc.		

LESS THAN 18 YEARS OF AGE

This section contains Lists of interest to people less than 18 years of age including youth, children and babies (or their parents.) All age groups need lists

Less Than 18 Includes These Lists:

CHILD / YOUTH BUDGET

MY DAILY CHORES

BEDROOM CLEANING CHART

CHORE IDEAS FOR CHILDREN

BACK TO SCHOOL SUPPLIES

CLASS AND ACTIVITY SCHEDULE

CLASS YEARLY SUMMARY

OUTFITTING THE NURSERY

WHAT TO PUT IN A DIAPER BAG

INSTRUCTIONS FOR THE BABYSITTER

CHILD / YOUTH BUDGET

MONTH OF _____		ESTIMATED INCOME ➡ (Allowance, Chores, Work)		$
You need money for these things	**#1 How much you think you'll spend**	**#2 How much you actually spent**	**Subtract column #2 from column #1**	**The difference**
1. Savings				
2. Education				
3. Lunch				
4. Bus fare				
5. School supplies				
6. Clothes & Shoes				
7. Recreation & Fun				
8. Music				
9. Food				
10 Personal care				
11. Gifts				
12. Vacation				
13. Dues				
14. Lessons				
15. Church				
		Add up the last column ➡		$

If column #1 is less than column #2, you are a good budgeter and probably had money left over.
If too many of your column #2s are more than column #1s, you probably ran out of money.
Look over your budget and see where you can save money.

MY DAILY CHORES

Make bed	Hang up clothes	Straighten room	Brush and floss teeth	Fix hair	Put on clean underwear	Put on clean clothes
School work	Take care of pets	Talk with family	Do chores	Read	Help with brother or sister	Eat good food
Play	Put away toys	Bath	Extra			

BEDROOM CLEANING CHART

Make bed	Clean under bed	Hang up or fold clothes	Straighten drawers	Put away shoes	Straighten closet floor	Closet door closed
Clean off dresser and desk	Dust furniture	Hang towels in bathroom	Vacuum or sweep floor			

CHORE IDEAS FOR CHILDREN

Feed and water pets	Scrub washbasins
Dust furniture	Polish appliances
Vacuum	Dust lights and picture frames
Set table or clear table	Clean light switches
Put away leftover food	Clean window sills
Sweep kitchen floor	Wipe off telephones
Wash the kitchen counters	Straighten books or magazines
Wash or dry dishes	Take out trash

BACK TO SCHOOL SUPPLIES

Binders	
Books and book covers	Report covers
Calculator	Ruler
Compass	Scissors
Construction paper	Stapler
Crayons	Tape
Erasers	And put it all in a backpack or school box
Glue or glue stick	
Hole punch	Extras:
Index cards	Clothes and Shoes
Markers	School Schedule
Notebooks	
Paint	
Paper (lined)	
Paper clips	
Pens and pencils (black & colored)	
Pencil sharpener	
Planning book with calendar	
Poster board	

Summary of Classes for Year_____

CLASS AND ACTIVITY SCHEDULE

Student Name:_____

Home Room Teacher:_____   Phone #_____

Date Semester Starts:_____ Semester Ends:_____

	List Class Times Under Each Day				
Below list: Subject / Teacher / Teacher Phone # / Other	**Monday**	**Tuesday**	**Wed**	**Thurs**	**Friday**
1.					
2.					
3.					
4.					
5.					
6.					
7.					
8.					
9.					
10.					

CLASS YEARLY SUMMARY

Subject & Final Grade			
First Term Semester/Quarter	**Second Term** Semester/Quarter	**Third Term** Semester/Quarter	**Fourth Term** Semester/Quarter
GPA	GPA	GPA	GPA

Comments / Notes	

OUTFITTING THE NURSERY

Furniture: Bassinet and Pad	**Feeding**: Bottles / Nipples / Liners
Chair (rocker or glider)	Bottle brush
Changing table	Breast pump
Crib and mattress	Burp cloths or cloth diapers
Dresser	Formula
Lamp and night light	Ice packs & cooler for trips
Nursery: Baby monitor	Plastic containers for freezing breast milk
Blankets, receiving and regular	**Traveling**: Backpack or sling
Books	Car seat
Bumper pad and accessories	Diaper Bag
Clothes hamper	Stroller
Diaper holder (for clean ones)	
Diaper pail (for dirty ones)	**Clothes**: Diapers (cloth and disposable)
Humidifier	Dresses
Mattress pad	Gowns
Mobile	Hats or headbands
Sheets for crib or bassinet	Pants
Sound machine	Rompers / Creepers / Diaper Sets
Swing	Shirts or tops
Bath Time: Comb and brush	Shoes / Socks / Tights / Booties
Nail clippers	Sleepers
Powder and lotion	Sweaters / Coats
Shampoo	Undershirts / Onesies
Soap	**Extras**: Medicine
Towel	Nasal aspirator
Toys	Thermometer
Tub	Tweezers
Washcloths	

WHAT TO PUT IN A DIAPER BAG

DIAPERS--Don't Forget These	Pacifiers
Bibs	Plastic bags
Blanket	Sunscreen
Bottles, Nipples, Liners	Sweater
Burp cloths	Toys
Changing pad	Water (for mom or mixing formula)
Clothes, extra outfits	Wet wipes
Diaper rash ointment	
Formula	
Hat	
Medicines	

For older babies add a cup, a snack or juice and waterproof pants.

INSTRUCTIONS FOR A BABYSITTER

NAMES AND AGES OF CHILDREN:	HOME Address:
	HOME Telephone #:
	NAME, ADDRESS AND PHONE NUMBER OF SCHOOLS:
ACTIVITY SCHEDULE FOR CHILDREN:	HOME ACTIVITY SCHEDULE :
	Meal Time
	Wake Up Time
	Nap Time
EMERGENCY CONTACTS:	Bed Time
My Cell Phone Number:	Television allowed these hours
My Pager Number:	Computer games allowed these hours
Neighbor	
Relative	NAMES OF APPROVED FRIENDS:
Pastor or clergy	
Doctor	
Veterinarian	NAME OF PETS:
SNACKS AND FOOD:	SPECIAL INSTRUCTIONS:
MEDICATIONS:	

The End Section Includes These Lists:

PLANNING A FUNERAL

GETTING A DIVORCE

REASONS TO GIVE UP

REASONS I CAN SUCCEED

Just as there are beginnings and happy times during life, there are the unpleasant aspects of living. The section called "The End" includes Lists with some unpleasant connotations. The thought of death or divorce or failure may activate painful emotions.

So many people have written to tell me how unpleasant it was to not know what the deceased wanted for their funeral, that I believe we may spare others some pain if we pre-plan the end of life. Divorce and the life-altering events that occur because of this change, also bring pain especially if we are unprepared for the many unpleasant tasks that must be completed.

Finally, many of you will read this book and never make the changes necessary to improve. For you, I've included a pre-made failure List called Reasons to Give Up. Although you probably have this List completed in your mind and you recall it often, I wrote it down so you could look at it and see how flimsy some of your excuses are. Also, I didn't want you to write down this negative list since that might reinforce your limiting beliefs about your ability to change. If you see yourself in the limiting beliefs on that page, put aside those reasons and change.

Instead of dwelling on the negative, you fill in the final List, Reasons I Can Succeed. It might stretch your abilities to find good reasons why you can overcome the limiting beliefs that have plagued you for so long. Start filling in that List and throughout the day, let your mind focus on other reasons you can succeed and add them to your Succeed List. Life should be treasured. Don't waste it by dwelling on the negative. Complete the final List in the book and keep it as a reminder of your ability to achieve.

Now it's time to turn this material over to you. I'll end the pages by letting you know you'll be happier if you get organized and you'll limit the frustrations in your life. Manage the muddle in your life and succeed one List at a time.

PLAN A FUNERAL

List preferences for your next of kin to follow.

☑		
NAME	ADDRESS	CITY/ STATE / ZIP
TELEPHONE #	RACE	SEX
DATE OF BIRTH	PLACE OF BIRTH	FATHER NAME
MOTHER NAME (MAIDEN)	SPOUSE NAME	SPOUSE TELEPHONE #
MARRIAGE DATE	MARRIAGE PLACE	DEATH DATE / PLACE OF SPOUSE
DIVORCE INFORMATION	OTHER SPOUSE INFORMATION	
NOTIFY CHILDREN: NAME	ADDRESS	TELEPHONE #
NOTIFY CHILDREN: NAME	ADDRESS	TELEPHONE #
NOTIFY CHILDREN: NAME	ADDRESS	TELEPHONE #
NOTIFY CHILDREN: NAME	ADDRESS	TELEPHONE #
NOTIFY FRIENDS: NAME	ADDRESS	TELEPHONE #
NOTIFY FRIENDS: NAME	ADDRESS	TELEPHONE #
NOTIFY FRIENDS: NAME	ADDRESS	TELEPHONE #

- Also complete: the Financial Information List
- the Medical Information List
- the Personal Information List

☑	INDICATE ONE PER CATEGORY		
	I PREFER • BURIAL • CREMATION	I PREFER • A MILITARY FUNERAL • A CHURCH FUNERAL • A GRAVESIDE SERVICE • NO SERVICES TO BE HELD	HOLD SERVICES AT • MORTUARY CHAPEL • CHURCH • CEMETERY • MAUSOLEUM
	VIEWING OF BODY • YES • NO • CASKET OPEN • CASKET CLOSED	I PREFER • AN OBITUARY IN LOCAL PAPER • NO OBITUARY • OBITUARY IN NAMED NEWSPAPER:	I PREFER • (STYLE OF CASKET OR URN)
	I PREFER • FLOWERS (TYPE) • DONATION TO ORGANIZATION:	I PREFER TO BE BURIED • WITH MY GLASSES ON • WITH MY GLASSES OFF • WITH THIS JEWELRY • WITH THESE MEMENTOS	I PREFER THESE MUSIC SELECTIONS • • • •
	I PREFER THESE PEOPLE SPEAK • • • • •	I PREFER THESE PEOPLE SAY PRAYERS • • •	I CHOSE AS PALLBEARERS • • • •

	NAME OF MORTUARY PREPAID PLAN? ACCOUNT #	NAME OF CHURCH / LOCATION	NAME OF PASTOR / CLERGYMAN
	NAME OF CEMETERY	LOCATION OF CEMETERY / PHONE	PLOT # AT CEMETERY
	OTHER BURIAL INFORMATION	MILITARY INFORMATION	ATTORNEY'S NAME / PHONE
	DESIGNATED PERSON TO EXECUTE THESE PREFERENCES	TELEPHONE / LOCATION	PHYSICIAN'S NAME / PHONE

I request that this plan be followed as closely as possible in executing my final arrangements.

_____

Signature   Date

GET A DIVORCE

Obtaining a divorce requires numerous lists and help from other people. This is only a brief starting point List that will give you some ideas to start this long process.

TO BE DONE	TARGET DATE	PERSONS INVOLVED
Pursue counseling with spouse to maintain the marriage. If it fails, continue with list.		
Pursue mediation instead of expensive legal litigation		
Jointly talk with children		
Inform family and friends		
Research attorney. Ask attorney: • How long have you practiced? • Are you a family practice lawyer? • How much is the retainer? Is it refundable? • Ask lots of questions about the cost and get a written proposal including hourly rates, other costs, estimate of the total cost of case. • See if lawyer has a payment schedule. • See if this lawyer likes to fight it out in court or settle cases. Will they consider meditation? • Who will be handling the case—the attorney, a partner or someone else • What is the estimated time frame? • Sign legal papers to retain attorney.		
Issues to be resolved: • Child support / child custody • Residence for both parties		

• Division of all vehicles with transportation for both parties • Joint business ventures • Debts on mortgages, loans , credit cards • Household furnishings / personal property division • Division of savings / stocks / cash • Pension and retirement plans • Support payments for spouse • Income tax returns • Division of insurance benefits • Educational expenses in the future • Estate / Trust funds • Pets		
Arrange for change of residence if needed		
Establish a separate checking account		
Keep copies of recent financial transactions (within 3 years if possible)		
Arrange for transportation needs		
Keep track of expenses during separation		
Have attorney go over financial paperwork		
Arrange for personal counseling if needed		

CHANGE YOUR NAME / CHANGE THESE DOCUMENTS

All insurance: Life / Health / Dental / Disability / Homeowners / Automobile

All joint ownership items: Automobiles / Home / Other registered vehicles

Financial plans: IRAs / Stock certificates / Brokerage accounts

Banks / Savings accounts / Credit union accounts

Safety deposit box

Credit cards / Debit cards / Department store credit cards / Gasoline company cards

Mortgages / Real estate

Loans / Contracts with monthly payments

Business ownership / Other joint ventures

Retirement plans

Doctors / Dentists / Therapists / Optometrist

Utility companies / Telephone companies / Cell telephone

Driver's license

Passport

E-mail address

Change passwords on Internet accounts

Wills / Power of attorney / Living will / Other legal documents

Stop automatic deposits

Documents with your employer relating to next of kin and benefit plans

Change of address (Use the Change of Address List)

Trust funds / Trust accounts

Estate planning documents

Anything else that had both your names on the account or named the spouse as beneficiary

REASONS TO GIVE UP ON GETTING ORGANIZED

1. I all ready know how to do this and I don't need anyone else's help.
2. I'm not good at following through with new projects.
3. I've never done well in school and I don't follow directions well.
4. I don't have the time to get organized.
5. I am learning disabled or physically disabled and my health is poor.
6. My home life is not conducive to undertaking any new tasks.
7. My job is so stressful that I can't take on anything else that is stressful or new.
8. I like to be spontaneous and decide what to do each day on the spur of the moment.
9. I don't make enough money and I know I'd have to buy items to get organized.
10. I've always been disorganized and I'm happy with the way things are in my life.
11. I've tried self-help programs and I fail when I try to implement them.
12. I make copies of the Lists and really intend to use them, but I put them aside and forget.
13. My old system for life management has worked for years.
14. I would have to change my habits.
15. I would have to try to change the habits of those who share my life.
16. Anytime I make changes in my life, there is a ripple effect that changes too many other things in my life.
17. I've tried to get organized before and it didn't work.
18. I would be the only one working to make this a successful system. No one else would help and they won't let me delegate to them.
19. I have too many children who are too young or too old or too something and my family would never get organized
20. I haven't succeeded at most programs I've tried whether to stop smoking or lose weight or become a positive thinker.
21. My 24 hours a day are filled to the brim with things I absolutely have to do and there are no sands of time left.
22. My home is small and there is no available space for change.
23. This is a bad time in my life.
24. It's winter and it's too cold, or it's summer and it's too hot.
25. I have no time, no energy, no money, I'm too old, too young.
26. I have a bookshelf full of self help books and my life hasn't changed other than I've wasted money on a shelf of books.
27. My family always has called me the "flaky" or disorganized person in the family.
28. I don't believe I can accomplish change to improve my life and surroundings.
29. I slog along in the mire each day, never making progress and sinking deeper with each step.
30. I've very self-critical and no level of accomplishment is enough.
31. I'm a perfectionist.
32. I'm obsessive-compulsive and overdo anything I try to achieve.
33. The List Organizer system does not appeal to my taste for getting organized..
34. The whole system is too complicated and I couldn't complete even one List.
35. I'm a negative thinker and criticize or make fun of those optimists who think change is easy or can be accomplished without hard work and suffering.
36. My limiting beliefs are too ingrained in my personality and it would be painful to give up those values that are the foundation of my perception of me.
37. I'm a failure—at almost everything I try.

REASONS I CAN SUCCEED AT GETTING ORGANIZED

I deserve good things to happen in my life.
2. My life will be less stressful, more peaceful.
3. This not only will help me but those who are close to me.
4. I'll probably save money by getting organized.
5. I'll feel a sense of accomplishment.

Now continue and complete this List. As you write down the reasons you can succeed, you will feel a sense that it is possible to change and become more organized. It's important to fill in this List to prove to yourself that you are capable to changing old habits.

I do not think there is any other quality so essential to success of any kind as the quality of **perseverance**. It overcomes almost everything, even nature. John D. Rockefeller
Our greatest weakness lies in giving up. The most certain way to succeed is to always try just one more time. Thomas Edison

Order Extra Books and Time Management Publications

P.O. Box 853
Hurricane UT 84737

Phone: 435-635-2314

Email: kaylee@listorganizer.

List Organizer—Simple Solutions for Complex Problems

Make Money Orders or Checks Payable to YMO

Products are available for sale on the Internet at www.listorganizer.com

Orders shipped only within the United States

<u>Lists for Muddle Management</u> **may be purchased as an e-book on the website—some foreign currencies accepted.**

Ship To:_____

_____

_____

_____

_____

Your e-mail address:_____

Purchase Order #:
Date:
Vendor ID:

Quan-tity	Item	Description—	Unit Price	Total
	#600	**Book-*Lists for Muddle Management***	$24.95	
	#605	**CD-Rom *Lists for Muddle Management***	$19.95	
	#205	**Meal Organizer**	$3.95	
	#305	**Travel Organizer**	$3.95	
	#505	**Budget Organizer**	$11.95	
	#230	**Grocery List-Category Check Off**	$3.95	
	#310	**Packing Lists**	$4.95	

			Subtotal	
			Tax (Utah)	
			Shipping	
			Total of Order	

Total of Order	Shipping Charges
$0.00—$10.00	$3.00
$10.01—$30.00	$5.00
$30.01—$60.00	$7.00
$60.01—$100.00	$9.00
$100.00—$200.00	$12.00